D1065165

Weather, Water and Boating

"When the Clouds Appear as Rocks and Towers,
The Sea Will be Refreshed by Frequent Showers."

Weather, Water and Boating

By

Donald A. Whelpley

Drawings by Carl W. Henry, Jr.

CORNELL MARITIME PRESS, INC.
Cambridge, Maryland
1961

Library of Congress Catalog Card Number: 61-12540
Manufactured in the United States of America

Contents

TO

BRAD AND ALAN

Preface

The sailor cannot escape from the elements, neither can he ignore weather, be it good, bad, or indifferent, because it surrounds him from the time he casts off until he bends on the last line at the dock and secures.

Skippers of rowboats and skippers of capital ships share many of the same weather problems, even if on a different scale. There is one thing about sailors and their weather information—they want it straight and to the point. And they want it to be practical; something they can put to use.

When I was young in meteorology and still carried away by the jargon of the trade, I learned a couple of good lessons about seamen and their weather from the salty captain of an aircraft carrier. Weather was vital to the operation of the ship and squadrons, but so were a lot of other things. The Old Man always had a lot on his mind, and did not tolerate much talk of "tropospheric double-bubbles and troughs aloft with positive vorticity." He wanted his weather information dispensed, staccato-like, in simple terms. It was good training for one in a field of endeavor notorious for equivocation.

The learning of the other lesson still makes me blush to recall it. One morning at sea, I arose and groped my way through the labyrinth of passageways connecting my stateroom with the weather office. The ship was an escort carrier and the weather office was two decks below daylight. The Old Man was already inquiring, via the intercom circuit, about the day's weather.

I glanced hurriedly at the weather map, checked the barometer and wind dials, and answered confidently, "We're in the trades, Captain. Excellent weather all day."

The squawk box seemed to ice over with the frostiness of the reply, "Then kindly come up to the bridge and explain this downpour!"

Thereafter, I always managed to go topside and have a look at the elements before making a forecast.

Weather charts covering large areas of the world are essential, but the weatherman—and the sailor—must also have a feel for what is going on in the sky and on the sea. That knowledge can be obtained only after many long hours of weather-watching, coupled with an understanding of what it is all about.

So, to make a long story short, what I have attempted to do in this book is to talk about weather problems of specific interest to sailors and to do so with a minimum of jargon. I have also tried to explain why weather behaves as it does, because this seems to me the first and most important step in becoming weatherwise. Emphasis has been steered more in this direction and less toward the inclusion of many tables, charts, and weather codes.

Appreciation is extended to Mr. Boris Lauer-Leonardi, editor of *The Rudder*, 575 Lexington Ave., New York 22, N.Y., and to the editors of *Frontiers*, the Magazine of the Academy of Natural Sciences of Philadelphia, 19th and the Parkway, Philadelphia 3, Penna., for use of material that originally appeared as articles in their magazines. Thanks to my wife, Pearle, who put in many hours of typewriter pounding to transcribe my illegible scribbling into readable form. I am especially grateful to my mother for sparking an early interest in the workings of the sky and sea—an interest that caused me to pursue the frustrating, but fascinating, science of meteorology.

All photographs are by the author, unless otherwise credited.

Donald A. Whelpley
Atlanta, Ga.

Chapter 1

Why the Weather?

"Now, we don't want any of that technical stuff," the spokesman was saying. "Just talk to us for a couple of hours about practical weather forecasting. You know, so we boatowners out there on the water can look around and tell what's going to happen."

It was the old, familiar refrain. The instructor had heard it from yachtsmen, aviators, Boy Scouts, the works. Everybody wanted to know about weather, but "not that technical stuff." They wanted a short, easy course that would make them expert forecasters. The instructor, a working meteorologist, would have liked that, too. He wished he could have learned meteorology that way years before, but he knew better. Weather is complex. He went through years of training to learn the fundamentals, and more years of experience to realize that he didn't know, by a long shot, all about the elusive mechanisms that control weather.

The instructor sympathized with those in his weather class. They worked all day at their jobs and came to class at night. After all, they were pursuing boating for pleasure, and weather was just one of the many things they needed to know. They had no desire to devote brain power to studying, and the meteorologist understood. At first, he tried to give his classes purely practical advice on weather, but he soon realized that the stuff he talked about was only superficial. The students still knew nothing. They failed to understand what caused the weather in their own immediate vicinity, much less over large areas. And, since local weather conditions are closely entwined with conditions throughout the atmospheric envelope that covers the earth, the only place to start was with the big picture.

The Sun is Responsible

The big picture goes far beyond the earth and its atmosphere, because the sun gets into the act in a major way. It is the sun's heat that is responsible for all weather. Without this intense heat supply, the air-cover of the world would simply sit, stagnant and unmoving. There would be no wind, clouds, or rain. It is the unequal heating of the earth that sets the air in motion, first in the general circulation, that large-scale movement that transports great masses of air vertically upward from the equatorial regions to descend at the poles, and then return across the earth's surface to complete the cycle.

Fig. 1. Simplified General Circulation of the Earth's Atmosphere

The Coriolis Force

The flow pattern of the general circulation in Figure 1 is over-simplified. This would be the picture if the earth did not rotate. But since it does rotate, then complications must be thrown in. One of the most significant effects caused by the rotating earth is the Coriolis force. Notice that in Figure 2 the mass air movement, as shown by the arrows, again goes up at the equator and heads poleward, but now it is turned to the right (to the left in the Southern Hemisphere) near latitudes 30 degrees N and S. Here the arrows crowd together.

We may as well polish off the Coriolis force now. It is one of those simple things that can be hard to grasp at first. But by using an ordinary phonograph turntable, and comparing it to one hemisphere of the revolving globe, the whole thing comes clearly into focus.

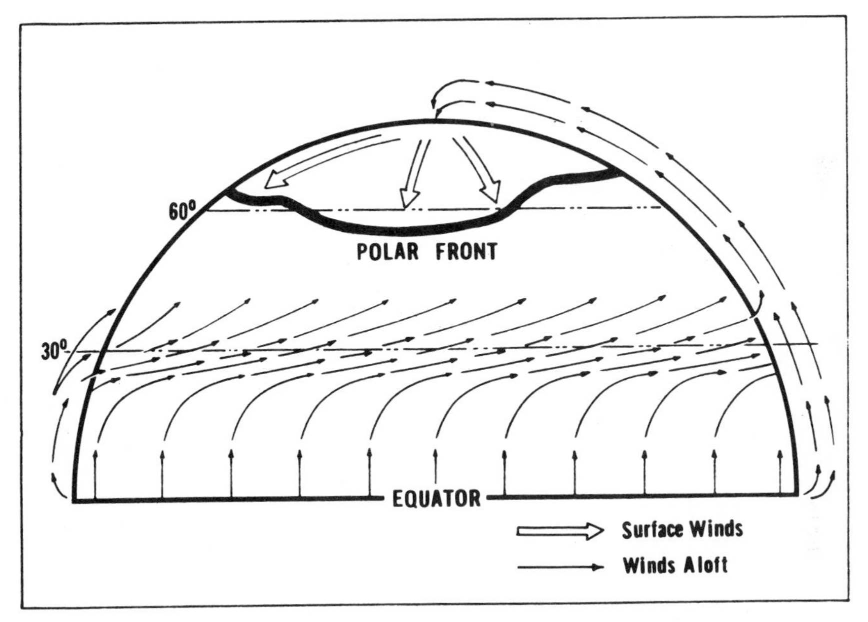

Fig. 2. General Circulation as Modified by the Earth's Rotation

Look down on the turntable and imagine that you are looking down on the earth. The center post is the pole and the outer rim of the disk is the equator. The phonograph turns clockwise, so its direction is opposite to the earth's rotation (when looking down from the North Pole) but for an illustration it is all right.

Take a piece of chalk and, starting at the "equator", move it across the turntable in a straight line to the center post, or "pole." When the turntable is stopped, you will see that you have drawn a curve rather than a straight line. The Coriolis force—an apparent force, not a real one—has made the line turn. Air moving over the earth takes this same curved path. The curve is to the right in the Northern Hemisphere, and to the left in the Southern Hemisphere.

Keep in mind that the air flow in Figure 2 is above the surface, say at 20 thousand feet or so. The convergence, or "packing," of the wind arrows causes air to pile downward near latitudes 30 degrees N and S to build a belt of high pressure at the surface. This belt is especially noticeable over the oceans, because the constant coolness of the seas enables the air to settle. The mariner's old and dear friend, the Bermuda *high,* is part of the belt.

Now the upper winds near latitudes 30 degrees N and S are blowing eastward, but they will work their respective ways around the earth and to the poles eventually. The paths of these strong upper winds are meandering, heading generally eastward, but for brief periods they snake about, going to the north, south, and occasionally even to the west. Frequently imbedded in these winds is the jet stream, a narrow "river" of air racing high over the earth.

Some of the winds at high levels will dip down to the ground between latitudes 30 and 60 degrees to blow as the "prevailing westerlies." The rest will stay aloft, later to subside at the poles to form polar *highs.* These frigid air masses will, in turn, drift equatorward over the surface. The boundary that separates them from more temperate air is the polar front, shown in Figure 3.

Cold and Warm Air Masses Battle

The polar front is an elastic, ever-changing barrier between heavy, cold air on one side and lighter, warmer air on the other. Now and then, it retreats poleward, only to charge forth again into temperate zones under the driving pressure of *highs* that refuse to be contained. At times, particularly in winter, it may barrel almost to the equator before the cold pushing air loses its strength.

Why does there have to be a front? A barrier? It is all air, whether cold or warm. Why doesn't the cold air of the polar *highs* just dribble down into warmer regions like water? Well, it is a matter of density. Cold and warm air masses vary in density in proportion to the temperature contrast between them. They just don't mix readily when there is as much as ten degrees difference, much less thirty or forty degrees.

Along the polar front, there is a constant battle between cold and warm air masses. Now we are getting closer to weather as the man on the street, or on deck, if you will, knows it. For it is these outbreaks of cold air, upon invading warmer territory, that battle with moist air and stir up great batches of weather.

The meteorological battleground is sporadic. On stretches of the polar front, all is quiet. Some sections are often "dry," with few clouds and no precipitation. Active weather is found mainly concentrated around the low pressure areas that are born, grow to maturity, and die on the polar front. Each *low*, during its lifetime, travels in an easterly direction, because in the temperate zones—the habitat of the extra-tropical cyclone—the guiding wind flow is from the west. It is this fact that forms the basis for weather forecasting. By spotting weather-making *lows* on the map, and following them as they plod along their rather predictable paths, we can forecast where they will go next to bring their own special brands of trouble.

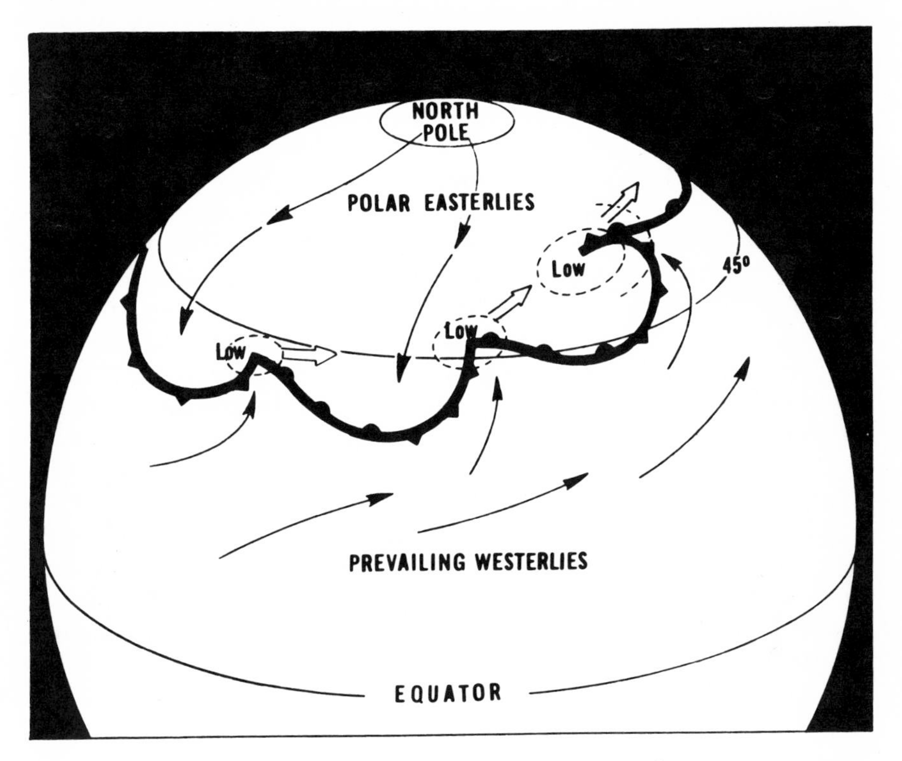

Fig. 3. The Polar Front Battleground

In Figure 3, there are three low pressure centers on the polar front. Each is in a different stage of development. Extra-tropical *lows*—incidentally, this term was coined to avoid confusion with tropical *lows*, or hurricanes—begin as weak waves on the polar front. They develop and become intense using moisture in the air for fuel.

Tracing a Typical Cyclone

Figures 4-1 through 4-6 trace the history of a typical cyclone from its inception to maturity. In Figure 4-1, a section of the polar front is advancing southeastward. It has penetrated deep into the temperate zone, and has slowed in forward movement because the cold air to the north has subsided, spread out over a large area, and no longer has the force it had on bursting out of the source region. Its source region was northwestern Canada. It could well have been Siberia, or the North Atlantic, or the North Pacific Ocean, as well as polar regions of the Southern Hemisphere.

Weather along our front is good. Some cloudiness, but not much. We will say the front is now nearing the lower Appalachian Mountains. The cold air behind the front is heavy and it hangs close to the ground. It is a shallow layer. So, when the front reaches the mountains, it bends because the cold air does not easily climb over the high terrain. This is pictured in Figure 4-2. This bulge in the front is the beginning of a new *low*. Bends in fronts, such as this one, are not always caused by mountains, although hills do the job well. Long, stretched-out cold fronts just naturally have their weak spots, and each weak section is a potential bend. An island at sea can accomplish it, or the sudden resistance of southerly winds confined to a narrow band can force a bend in the front.

Once a warm wedge has pushed its way into the wall of cold air, as in Figure 4-3, action begins. The warm air is lighter than the cold, and it is surrounded on three sides by heavier air. The warm air is squeezed and it rises. Clouds and precipitation result because of expansional cooling of the upward moving air. Barometric pressure is lowered in the bulge. Now that there is a low-pressure center, however weak, the air flow tends to turn into this center. The wind, if left to its own devices, would like to flow directly in and fill the low pressure. But our old friend, Coriolis, appears and makes the wind veer to the right. The suction of the low pressure pulls it back and, after a brief tug of war between low pressure and Coriolis force, the air flow settles into a steady counterclockwise (in the Northern Hemisphere) motion around, and slightly into, the center of the *low*.

In Figure 4-4, a band of precipitation has popped up on the northeast side of the wave, as the system is called. The precipitation is of the overrunning type, caused by warm air riding up over the cold air.

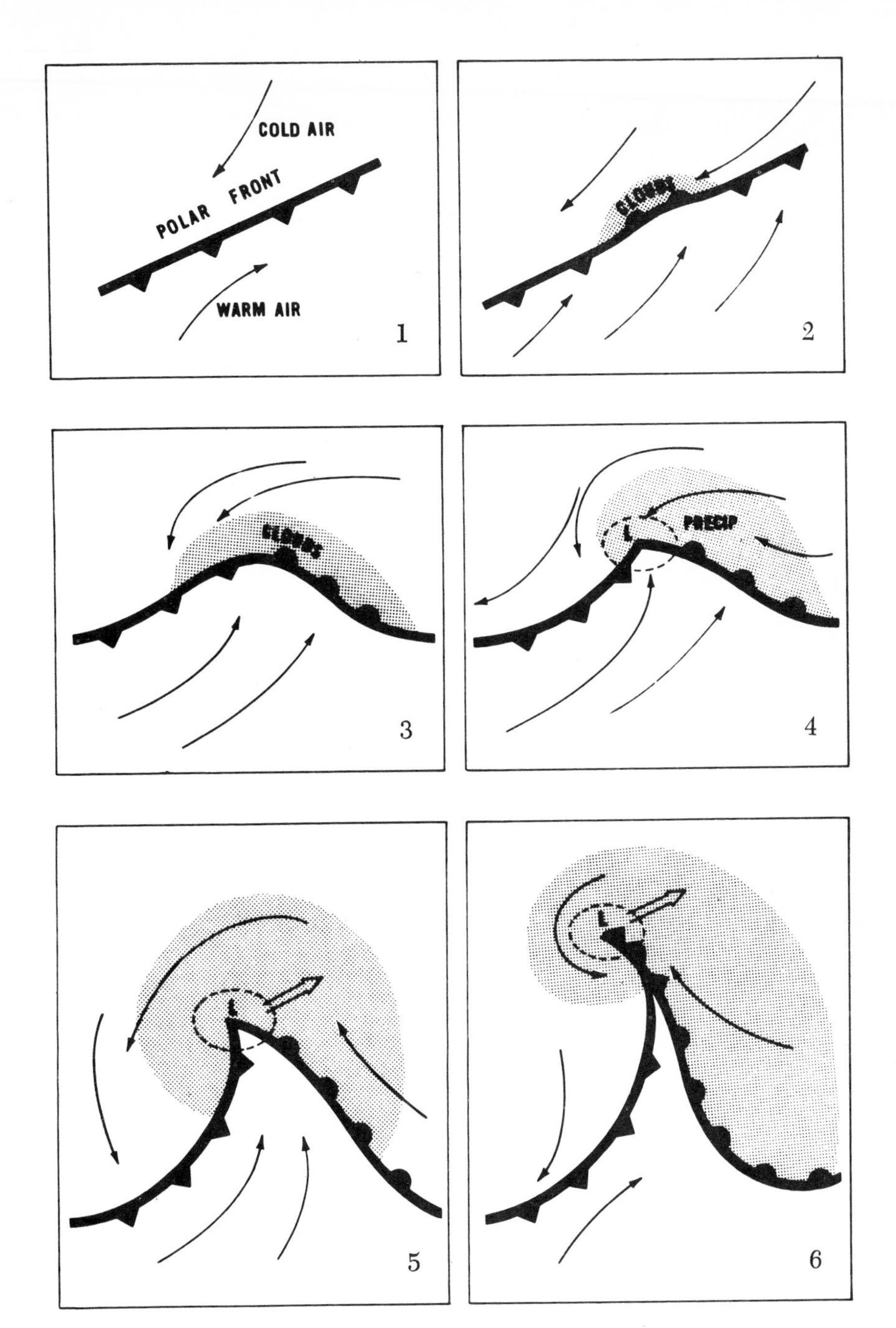

Fig. 4. Life Cycle of a Low Pressure Area

Now the weather machine is cranked up and going. It will continue to develop, getting bigger and more active. Twelve hours have elapsed since the first bend appeared in the front. Another five days or so will pass before the storm dies somewhere in the North Atlantic.

In the meantime, our cyclone will bring wind and rain across a wide swath of the country. Snow, sleet, and freezing temperatures will accompany it in winter. When the storm goes to sea, ships will be battered by the waves churned up by its winds. These winds will normally reach a highest velocity of 30 to 40 knots at sea, and 20 to 30 knots over land. Every *low* is different, however, and we cannot very well assign normalcy to cyclones. Summer *lows* might stir up breezes of a mere 10 knots, whereas the severest of winter storms have roared over the land with sustained hurricane-force winds.

Notice that in Figure 4-5 the slice-of-pie-like wedge of the warm sector is being compressed, reduced in size. Heavy air pushing down behind the *low* moves faster than the light, warm air, so the cold front is overtaking the warm front. In Figure 4-6, this overtaking has progressed to the point of "occlusion." Cold air is actually pushing the warm air aloft. Soon, only cold air will surround the *low*, and thus robbed of its nurturing energy supply, the cyclone will deteriorate.

Anticyclone

After a low pressure system has moved on, then what? Another *low* will, in due time, come along with its attendant weather, but in the meantime, sandwiched in between successive *lows*, there will be a mass of cold air, an anticyclone.

High pressure areas are not complex. On the contrary, nothing on the weather map is simpler. A *high* is approximately circular, or oval shaped, and covers a good bit of real estate. It is composed of air all from one source region, and this air is homogeneous. Of course, a hunk of air as large as that which comprises a typical anticyclone extends over wide areas; it is subject to varying amount of heat from the sun and modifying effects of land and water. So, the air on the east side of a *high*, for example, is bound to be different from that on the west side. But these changes are gradual. There is no sharp conflict, no fronts. Weather is good throughout the *high* for this reason, plus the fact that the air is subsiding, slowly descending. This means it is drying out and becoming more stable.

(Official U. S. Navy Photo.)

When a Low Pressure Area Goes to Sea, Ships are Battered by Waves Churned Up by Its Winds

You cannot make a definite statement about weather without ringing in an exception or two, so here are a couple to contradict the above. Occasionally, a high pressure area is made up of cold, heavy air that is very shallow. Warm air flowing over the top of this thin layer acts like a warm front, and right in the middle of the *high* there might be overcast skies and precipitation. This never fails to disconcert student weathermen.

Again, it is possible to find a summer anticyclone rife with thunderstorms. The *high* must be weak and old for this to happen. The air has become humid and hot, and by this time it is actually no longer a high pressure area, except by comparison with even hotter, lighter air around it.

So that is the big picture—the general circulation of air around the earth, and the secondary circulation of *lows* and *highs* that make our weather. To pin down the real purveyors of weather change, we need to look closely at fronts and air masses.

Chapter 2

Fronts and Air Masses

Not so long ago, fronts were not a part of the weatherman's language. Pressure systems were drawn on the weather map with only isobars (lines of equal barometric pressure). Forecasts of weather were issued on the basis of which quadrant of a cyclone, or an anticyclone, the observer was expected to be in. It was conceded that the northeast quadrant of a *low* held weather that was cool and sloppy. Low clouds, rain, and fog were in order. The western quadrants were expected to be cold and dry, with gusty winds. Now and then, a daring analyst would sketch in a "wind shift line" extending from the low pressure center, and point out that along this line there would be showers, followed by clearing and colder weather. This, of course, was the cold front. But meteorologists of twenty-five and more years ago did not think in terms of fronts and air masses; not many of them, at any rate.

Air Mass Analysis

There were a few in Norway who, during World War I, observed that masses of air could be classified in several categories, based on their places of origin. They saw that these nomadic masses guarded the properties acquired in their source regions jealously, and that these properties, such as temperature, moisture, and stability were the real causes of changeable weather. The next step in their reasoning was to note that there must be sharp dividing boundaries between air masses of different qualities. These were called fronts. The entire technique of the Norwegians was termed "air mass analysis."

It is as simple as it sounds. We just analyze the large bulks of air from reports on the weather map, assign each a type name, separate them by fronts, find out where they have been and where they are going, and make forecasts accordingly.

The U. S. Navy was one of the pioneers of air mass analysis in this country. Navy weathermen were drawing fronts on their weather maps before other meteorologists in the United States. And now, air mass analysis is here to stay. But before going on to air mass types, let us look at fronts.

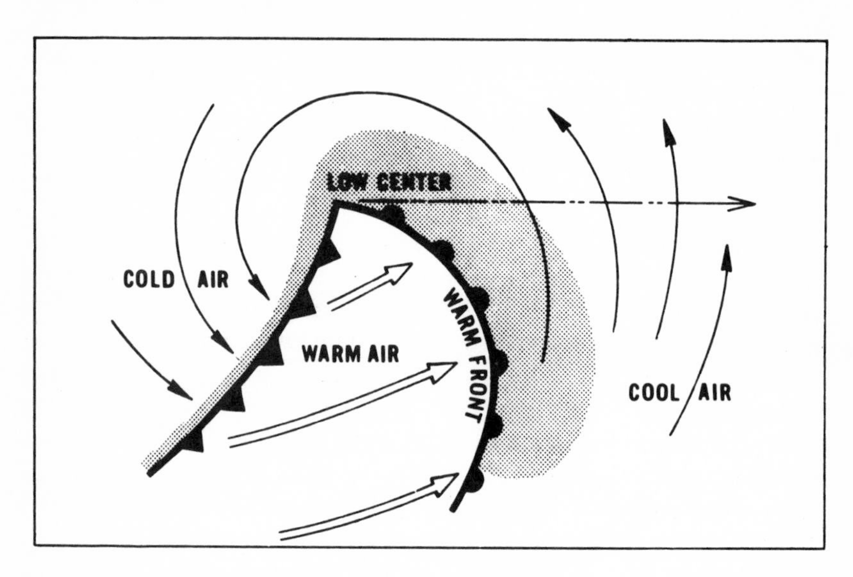

Fig. 5. A Typical Cyclone

Cold and Warm Fronts

A model of the typical mature cyclone is pictured in Figure 5. Three distinct types of air surround the system, and the differences in these air masses cause the *low* to retain well-defined fronts. Remember, air of contrasting densities does not mix. The cold air rushing in from the northwest advances with a sharp forward wall, the cold front, pushing against the warm air coming up from the south. The impact along this frontal line produces weather that is "sharp." Heavy showers, thunderstorms, and gusty winds are typical. Clearing usually follows a few hours after the front has swept through. Figure 6 is an idealized cold front.

On the other hand, warm air, in its encroachment upon the cool air of the northeast quadrant of the *low*, eases up and over. This makes for a much wider band of cloudiness and precipitation. In Figure 7, the precipitation has been left off to keep from confusing the scene, but rain, snow, or sleet, would be falling from the clouds all the way from the surface warm front position to the altostratus deck. The warm front at the surface is actually several hundred miles behind the leading edge of warm air, which soars twenty thousand feet up. It is this high level flow that generates cirrus clouds and gives early warning of the storm's approach. Even if more widespread, warm frontal weather is gentler because the conflict between the air masses is less abrupt. Long-lasting, steady, and usually light, "winter" rains belong to the warm front.

Sketches of fronts in meteorology books are all similar. They show idealized structure, complete with standard cloud and precipitation patterns. There can be no quarrel with this because in order to convey the picture of typical frontal weather, some array must be settled on. The fact is each front has its own personality, just as do *lows*, and each so differs from the typical that when a "textbook" front is sighted by meteorologist, aviator, or mariner, it is subject for shop talk.

Many variables go to make up the character of a front, and seldom do all of these coincide in just the right proportions to produce "standard" fronts. Nevertheless, idealized frontal pictures serve an important purpose. The thing to keep in mind is that there are differences in each front. Just because a cold front is expected to pass, it must not be assumed that you are bound to be socked by a thunderstorm, and that the sky will clear, on schedule, an hour or so later. Cold fronts in diagrams are shown to have thunderstorms because most cold fronts do. But many go through life with nothing more than scattered light showers. Some are dry, without precipitation or clouds.

It all depends on the moisture content of the air masses in conflict. If both the cold and the warm masses are dry, nothing will happen; no clouds, no precipitation. If the warm air is moist, but the invading cold air very dry, as it often is, weather will accompany the front, but clearing will be rapid after the front has passed because cloudiness and showers cannot exist in air of low humidity. If the warm air is "loaded", very wet in depth, stand by for trouble. Heavy clouds and lots of precipitation will result as the warm air is forced aloft by the moving wedge of cold air. Couple this with a damp, cold air mass, and bad weather will trail far behind the leading edge of cold air.

Other variables are: stability of the air masses involved, speed of advance of the front, and the slope of the front.

Atmospheric Stability

What is meant by stability? This is a bit of jargon often bantered around by weathermen. If a layman gathers up enough nerve to inquire about it, he is quickly put in his place by a flurry of talk about pseudo adiabatic lapse rates and inversions. But it need not be complex. Atmospheric stability depends on one thing only—temperature in the vertical. Air is stable when temperature increases with altitude (this is an inversion), or decreases slowly. Air is unstable when temperature falls off rapidly aloft. Here is the reason.

Warm air is lighter than cold air and wants to rise. During stable conditions, this lifting is stopped by a layer of air above that is warmer than the air below it; hence, no upward movement—status quo. Now, when the warmest air is at the surface, it goes up and continues to rise as long as it is warmer than surrounding air. It is this vertical motion, or lack of it, that determines the stability of an air mass. Why? Well, atmospheric pressure, due to density of the air, always reduces steeply upward. So, a column of air going up undergoes rapid expansion because of less and less pressure on it. As it expands, its moisture condenses to form, first clouds, then precipitation. If it keeps rising, larger raindrops form. These drops cannot hold together beyond a certain size, and consequently split. When this happens, electrical charges are generated, and a thunderstorm is the result. Aircraft pilots are more concerned with stability than are sailors, because their safety depends on the stability of the upper air. Airplanes have been torn asunder by violent updrafts. No boat has ever been ripped apart by an unstable air current, but, even so, boatmen should understand stable and unstable weather.

Meteorologists find out about vertical temperature distribution by using radiosonde balloons. Helium-filled rubber balloons carrying small, expendable radio transmitters are sent up twice daily from 75 or so locations in the United States. Temperature, humidity, and air pressure readings are relayed back to ground stations and this information is dispatched by teletype so that stability conditions for the entire country are available to forecasters.

Characteristics of Cold and Warm Fronts

So far we have talked more of cold fronts than of other members of the frontal family. This is understandable while on the subject of stability and its effect on weather in fronts, because cold fronts exert an impact on the air being displaced, and the associated

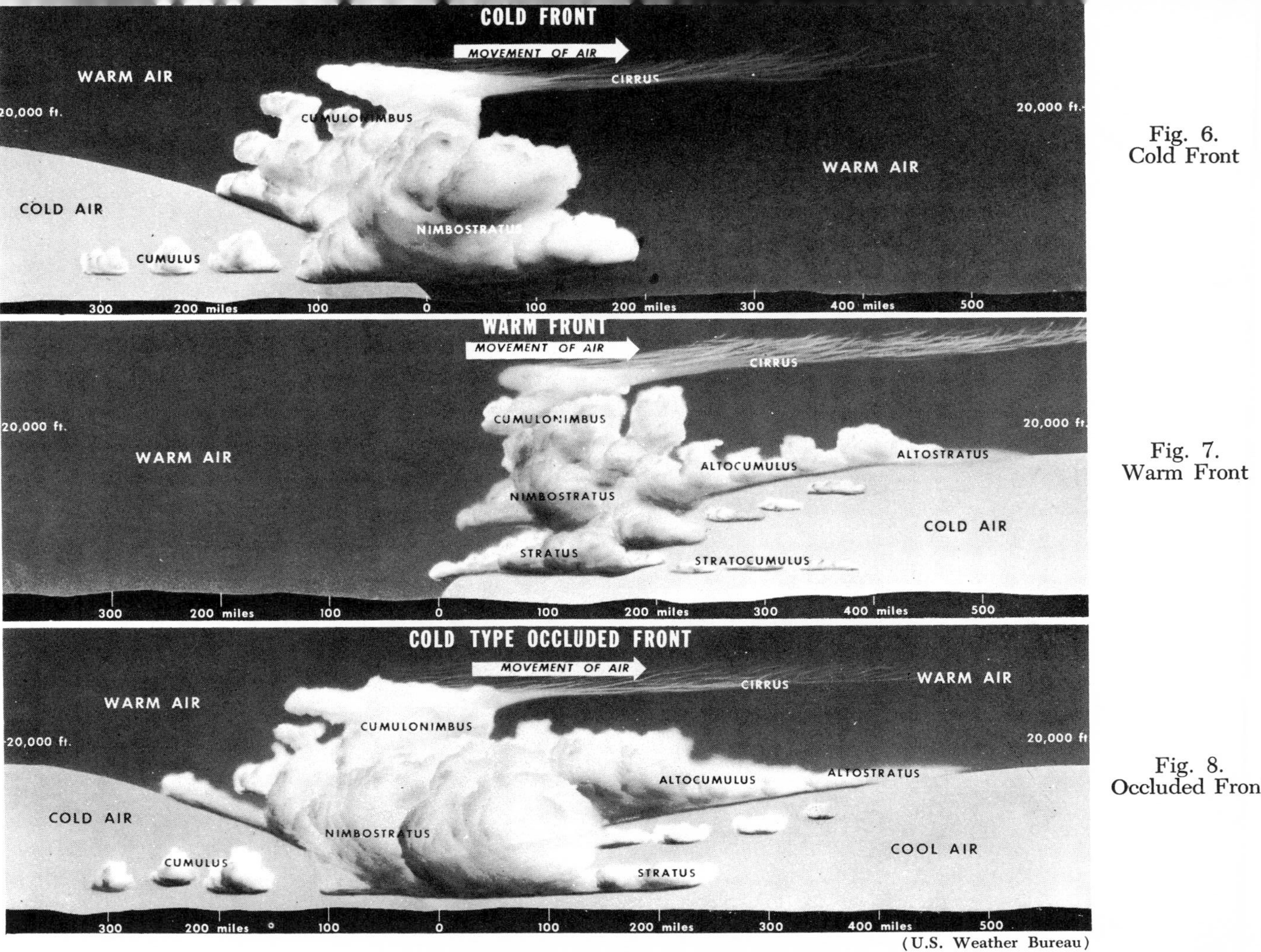

Fig. 6.
Cold Front

Fig. 7.
Warm Front

Fig. 8.
Occluded Front

(U.S. Weather Bureau)

weather acts accordingly. Even though warm fronts lack the impact factor, and weather in them is gentler because of the easy up and over motion of the warm air, stability still must be considered. If this warm air gliding upward is unstable, there will be thunderstorms, but these are high off the ground. The strong downdrafts of wind usually rushing out of thunderclouds just do not reach the surface from warm frontal thunderstorms.

As for speed of movement, again cold fronts take the spotlight. They move faster than warm fronts, in almost every case, and because of the impact factor, this is important. No matter how fast a warm front moves, the upward flow of air is gentle. But with cold fronts, the speedier they are, the rougher the weather.

A typical cold front will move at about 15 knots. Some merely creep forward, and an occasional one will scoot over the countryside at 50 knots or more. They are faster in winter than in summer. Warm fronts travel at about half the velocity of the cold fronts on the same weather map, and this leads to their being overtaken by the more rapidly advancing cold fronts. The result is a combination, or occluded front, shown in Figure 8. Refer to Figure 4-6 for the overtaking process.

Occlusions

For the purposes of studying weather on the surface, we will consider only cold type occluded fronts. They may be lumped together with cold fronts because they behave alike. There are two types of occlusions, cold and warm, but unless you are an aviator and expect to be up among them, there is no need to go into the details. Briefly, a cold type occluded front results when air behind the cold front is colder than any other air mass surrounding the *low*. This is the normal situation, so cold type occlusions predominate. Now and then, it happens that the air mass pushing the cold front, while cold, is not as cold as the air on the east side of the cyclone. So when the occluded front forms, it is of the warm type.

The sailor need know only this about occluded fronts: they are much like cold fronts, except that the associated cloud and precipitation is a bit more widespread.

When it comes to knowing how much slope there is to a front, the casual glancer at a weather map is completely in the dark. So is the professional meteorologist many times. The line separating air masses of different properties is easy to detect on the surface, but remember the frontal line on the weather map is two-dimensional only. That third dimension, the vertical, is the puzzler. An

Fig. 9. A Cold Front At Sea

idea of just how the front slopes aloft can be gained by such things as how far ahead of a surface warm front, or how far behind a surface cold front, the cloudiness and precipitation extend. Obviously, a steep front means a narrow band of weather, and a shallowly sloping front will have a broad weather zone.

On the average, the slope of cold fronts is 50 to 1, and warm fronts 125 to 1. So, if a warm front is approaching and the clouds are 5000 feet up, then the surface front is 100 miles or so away. Fast moving fronts have steeper slopes than creepers. The slope becomes more gradual as the front gets older.

Dew Point

For the sailor on deck who suspects a frontal passage but does not have a weather map handy, here are a couple of checks. The surface wind will shift clockwise when a front passes. With a cold front, the shift will be from a southerly to a westerly, or northerly, direction. Velocity will usually increase with the passage. A warm front passing causes the wind to veer from an easterly to a southerly quadrant. Change in wind speed will be less noticeable. Temperature and dew point will drop after the cold front, and climb behind the warm front. Meteorologists are more concerned with dew point than actual air temperature, because temperature is a changeable thing, subject to the whims of time of day and cloudiness. But dew point is conservative. It remains nearly constant in an air mass.

Air Mass Types

Forecasters detect air masses and track them by using the reports on weather maps. They know the source regions and the paths that principal air masses follow. These are pictured in Figure 10. They can judge the qualities of each air mass from daily observations of weather reporting stations in the path of the migrating air. From this information they make forecasts for conditions at places yet to be affected by these masses. To identify air masses, a universal form of shorthand is in use, a method of classifying them according to their place of origin and relationship to the area over which they travel.

First, and most important, is the climatic zone of the source region. There are four classes:

A—Arctic air masses (the coldest)

P—Polar air masses (cold)

T—Tropical air masses (warm)

E—Equatorial air masses (the warmest and wettest)

Lest there be some confusion about Arctic and Polar types, Arctic air comes from a higher latitude than Polar air. Perhaps more appropriate tags could be used, but we are stuck with these by virtue of long usage.

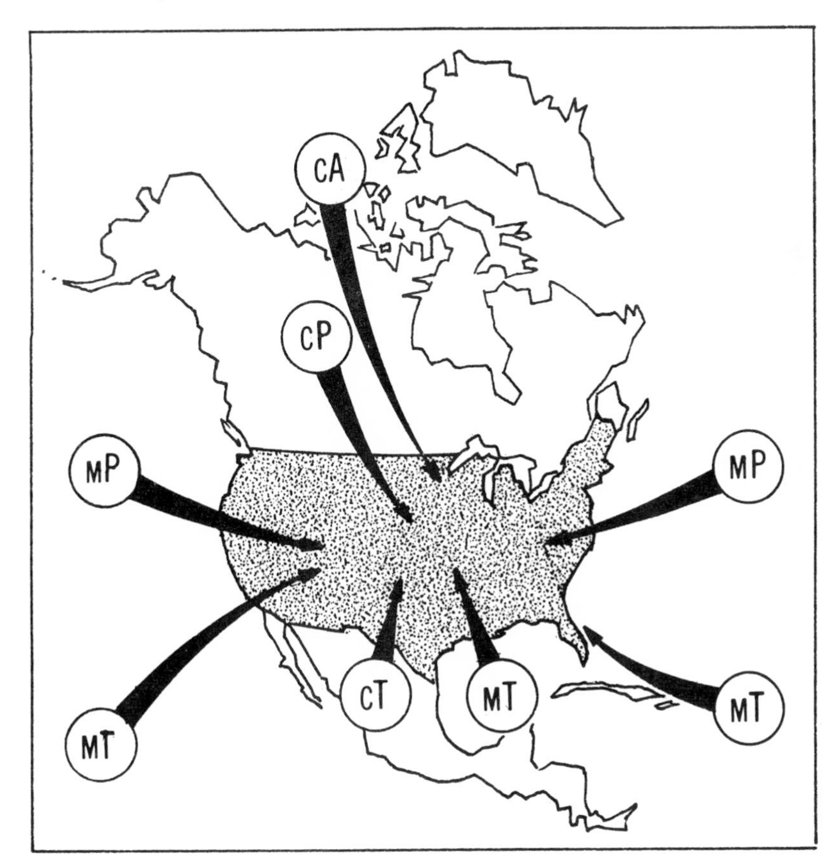

Fig. 10. Sources of Air Masses That Invade the United States

A glance at the air mass type tells us a great deal about its characteristics, but to further qualify it, a prefix and an affix are added. The prefix is an *m* or a *c*, indicating that the source was either maritime or continental. A maritime influence tends to tone down extremes of temperature, so a maritime polar air mass would be cold and moist, but not nearly as cold as continental polar air.

Likewise, continental tropical air is dry and unusually hot. Air of maritime tropical origin is warm and moist. That never-fail global thermostat, the sea, can be depended upon to work its temporizing wonders. Equatorial air is rarely found in this country. Occasionally some of this humid air will make its way northward to Florida or the Gulf coast. Since equatorial masses are almost all of ocean origin, no prefix or affix is needed. Just the letter *E* tells the uncomfortable story.

The third letter in air mass designations is affixed to tell whether the air is warmer (*w*) or colder (*k*) than the area it is invading. This makes a lot of difference because the temperature differential determines stability. Air masses of the *w* type are stable. Warm air overruning a colder surface "puts a lid" on any vertical movement. Clouds are stratiform, and precipitation, if any, is steady and general. Visibility is usually reduced by moisture and haze trapped under the strong inversion promoted by the warm air aloft. This is good "fog air," especially as it moves into colder regions. Winds in *w* air are smooth and steady.

Air colder than the surface, *k* type, is unstable. There is no lid on vertical movement, and low level haze and moisture are thoroughly mixed aloft so that visibility is excellent. For fog to form in this air is rare indeed. Clouds in *k* air are cumuloform and precipitation is showery. Surface winds are strong and gusty.

Listed here are the principal air masses that affect the United States, with a brief description of their source regions and characteristics.

cAk—Continental Arctic air, colder than the surface over which it lies. The source of this air mass is the ice covered region within the Arctic Circle. This intensely cold air does not often push far beyond the northern border of the United States, but when it does, there can be little question that winter has come. It is dry and has a penetrating, heavy feel. Sound does not transmit well.

mAk—Maritime Arctic air, colder than the ground or sea. Source region is the unfrozen seas within or near the Arctic Circle. This is also very cold air, but not quite as extreme as *cA*. The moisture content is higher, however, and it has a dull, leaden, unpleasant feel.

cPk—Continental Polar, colder than the area it is invading. The source of this air is central and northwestern Canada, primarily, although occasionally *cP* builds up in the central and western United States. This cold dry air is the normal "cold outbreak" of winter, and brings pleasantly cool spells in summer. More than any other air mass type it dominates weather in the United States. It is responsible for October's "bright blue days" and the frost on the pumpkin. When not too cold, it has an enervating quality, a zing. During the first few days of welcome respite from summer heat, *cPk* air is pleasant, but after it has settled down to stay, it becomes oppressive. The mass is dry, so showers and thunderstorms do not form. But it picks up humidity in the lower levels from the surface, and while this is not enough to allow cooling showers, it is enough to make things uncomfortable.

mPw—Maritime Polar air, warmer than the land. This mass is born at sea, either over the Atlantic or Pacific, and drifts inland where it is warmer than the ground. Obviously it was not too cold to begin with. A typical wintertime temperature might be 50° F. But it is moist, and its *w* characteristic makes it stable. Cloudiness is plentiful, and some light precipitation can be expected, especially in the West where it climbs over the Rockies. This air has a damp chilly quality that feels of the sea, even far inland. Visibility is usually poor, and fog comes easily.

mPk—Maritime Polar air, colder than the surface over which it is passing, originates in the colder sections of the oceans. It is never very cold, but does have a high moisture content. Showers are plentiful because of the instability. This air mass enters the United States more frequently in spring than any other season, and at this time of year it is almost balmy, with a "soft" feel—not too cold.

mTw—Maritime Tropical air, warmer than the surface. This warm, balmy air comes from the Gulf of Mexico and tropical areas of both oceans. It is drawn northward by large low pressure areas, and sometimes travels as far from home as Canada. It is moist and stable, and is loaded with low stratus clouds and light showers. But, when lifted by a cold front or squall line, the rain can be heavy and prolonged. There is more than enough water vapor available for many thunderstorms. Next to *cPk* air, this kind is found most in the United States. In winter, it brings occasional touches of spring to frozen parts of the country. This condition does not last long, though, because a cold front is usually nearby,. ready to return conditions to normal. Maritime tropical air has a "lilting," springlike feel. Sound carries far and wide. There is no mistaking *mTw* air when it arrives.

mTk—Maritime Tropical air, "colder" than the land. Obviously, this is an unusual type, although it does happen more often than would be imagined. It is a summer phenomenon, and the air is of the trades. Coming from a source where water temperatures are not excessive, *mTk* flows onto hot land areas, and acquires its *k* classification. This air mass is really quite delightful. Summer temperatures remain in the 80's, and because of its instability, showers and thunderstorms are frequent. This holds down the temperature. The air is washed by the showers, and brilliantly white cumulus clouds appear as if etched on the bright blue of the sky. Humidity is not unusually high.

One thing to keep in mind is that as soon as air masses leave their source regions, they begin to modify. This is a fortunate thing, for a *cAk* mass with temperatures of 40° below zero would be most unwelcome in Florida. Cold air modifies more rapidly and to a greater extent than warm masses. The cold air only has to gain heat from the ground and sun, and moisture from the earth, lakes, and the sea. But warm air must lose heat and water vapor, and this is a tougher job.

Despite these modifications, air masses retain their identity for several days. Only after five days or more over a warm ocean does polar air become tropical, and then only in the lower levels.

"Smelling the Weather"

Most meteorologists will not admit publicly that air masses have a feel and smell, but privately they will own up to it. Countless times forecasters have pinned down the position of a "lost" front by stepping outside and smelling the weather. It is a pretty good practice, as generations of seafarers have confirmed. Each air mass has its own personality. Have you not experienced days in spring or summer that brought poignant memories of an autumn cruise; or a day in midwinter that had an aura of spring—made you want to start fitting out?

It is not just the temperature that conveys the impression, but the buoyancy of the air, and the way sound carries. A maritime air mass that has penetrated deep into the midwest can take a homesick sailor back to the sea in a flash. And, if a whiff of the odor of creosote floats by, all he need do is to close his eyes to be on the docks of some distant seaport once more.

CHAPTER 3

The Weather Map and a Tale of Three Cities

The morning of April 2, 1952 broke crisp and clear at St. Louis. Spring had definitely arrived. The elms and willows along the banks of the river were green with new buds. The Mississippi rolled sluggishly by, swollen from rains and melted snow.

Spring had come, and yet there was a touch of winter in the air. A fresh outbreak of continental Polar air had swept down over the plains two days earlier, and now the *high*, the center of the air-mass dome, was centered over Oklahoma, a few hundred miles away. St. Louis was caught between the northeast quadrant of the *high*, and a deep low pressure system just to the north of the Great Lakes, as shown in Figure 11-1. The pressure gradient, or spacing of the isobars, was still "tight," so a resulting brisk northwest wind gave the *cPk* air an extra bite.

The *low* to the north was dying, but had not completely lost its punch. Snow showers swirled across the Great Lakes, driven by 25 knot winds. There was no pleasure boating on the lakes this day.

The *low* had been a real rip-snorter two days before when it bruised its way up through the midwest. With a central pressure of 989.0 millibars (29.20 inches) and gales of 50 knots, it was one of the last defiant gestures of winter. Later cyclones would become gradually more gentle, in keeping with the softer weather of spring.

The storm was dying because it had occluded, and only cold air surrounded the core. The occluded front extended from the center ESE'wd to a point off the Atlantic coast. Here a new low pressure center was forming, nourished by warm, moist air from the Gulf Stream. The cold front—the leading edge of the *cPk* air over the central United States—had moved rapidly offshore and was now at sea off Florida. This front had slowed in its eastward advance, and was about to stop altogether. The reason: the cold *high* was losing its force, flattening out. Its source of supply, cold air pouring down from above much like sugar from a scoop, was cut off. So it exerted less push on its extremity, the cold front.

Meteorologists watched these events through the ubiquitous eyes of the teletype machines, hourly clattering out a never-ending stream of coded numbers representing weather observations from a vast network of reporting stations. They plotted the reports on their weather maps and waited. A growing uneasiness crept into their thinking. Their pace quickened a bit from the leisure that accompanies "*cPk* weather." Aviation forecasters in the midwest began preparing for action. The weather was beautiful in their domain now, true, but one fact made them realize that aircraft traffic would soon be hampered. Barometric pressures were falling at a goodly clip throughout the *high*. If good weather was to continue, these pressures should be rising, or, at least, holding their own.

A St. Louis boatowner with a couple of spare days on his hands drove down to the yacht basin to inspect his cruiser. Spring, with its green grass and budding trees, made him want to get underway for a short trip down the river, maybe as far as Cape Girardeau. That would take a full two days. But as he puttered around his craft, he noticed that the barometer was dropping. It had gone down four points in an hour and, being weatherwise, he figured he had better call the Weather Bureau.

No, said the forecaster, the fine weather would not hold beyond tomorrow. As he talked, he put the finishing touches on his weather map. He drew in a dashed blue and red line, running north-south from Mexico to Canada. This stationary front extended from western Texas through eastern Colorado, into a weak *low* in Montana. No weather in the front now except cirro-stratus clouds, but pressures were falling fast in the whole area. Then he sketched in a blue line, a cold front, in the Rockies. This was the forward boundary of a fresh Polar outbreak swooping down out of Canada. Pressures were rising steeply over the mountains. Trouble was brewing. The time was 1230 CST (1830Z), April 2.

Down in Tampa, Florida, spring was no novelty. It had been around since early March. The azaleas had burst out in their scarlet glory, but had long since faded and gone. Boating was in full swing and Tampa Bay was alive with everything from outboards to big yachts. Out in the Gulf, Spanish mackerel were running in great schools.

April 2 was a fine day in Tampa. The air was cool and dry after passage of a cold front the night before. This brand of weather, coupled with a west wind and rising barometer, put everybody at ease. Meteorologists saw the same events taking place over the foothills of the Rockies that their midwestern cohorts saw, but refused to let it bother them. They had at least two more days of good weather. The Oklahoma *high*, even though weakening, still had to push across to the north of Florida before anything would set in.

Winter had not yet released its grip on New York. A raw northwest wind blew into the new *low* just offshore. Cold rain had fallen, ending a few hours before when the occluded front passed on its way northward. The air was still damp and promised to remain so for another twelve hours because it came from over the Great Lakes in a cartwheeling path around the deep cyclone over Lake Superior.

Continental Polar air had moved into the New York area with the occluded front. It replaced an *mPk* air mass dragged ashore from the north Atlantic by the pull of the deep *low*. New York weathermen were calling for better weather, based on the central-U.S. *high* drifting eastward and cutting off the flow of damp, cold air from over the lakes.

The night passed and by 0730 EST (1230Z), on April 3, weather at New York did, indeed, improve. *See* Figure 11-2. The Lake Superior cyclone had filled radically, and now the slackened flow of wind around it was turning in more to the center. The storm, what was left of it, was keeping the cold air to itself. This allowed a "nose" of the now egg-shaped *high* to poke into the New York area and bring in drier air.

The dome of the *cPk* air mass was now centered over Chattanooga, and it was cold for April. Early morning temperatures were in the thirties in Tennessee and northern Alabama. The dense air of the *high* was subsiding, and this was evident even to the layman. Meteorologists knew by the reduction in barometric pressure. The central isobar was now 1020 millibars (30.12 inches). Yesterday it was 1023 millibars (30.21 inches). The layman could tell by the feel of the air and appearance of the sky. The day seemed more like autumn. The sky was blue, but there was a soft look to it, caused by smoke and haze accumulating under the subsidence inversion, or warm layer above.

Even in Tampa, April 3 had more of a fall atmosphere than that of spring. Whereas the day before the new *cPk* air mass was unstable and buoyant, today it was stable and smooth. The wind, light in force, had veered around to the north to follow the isobaric

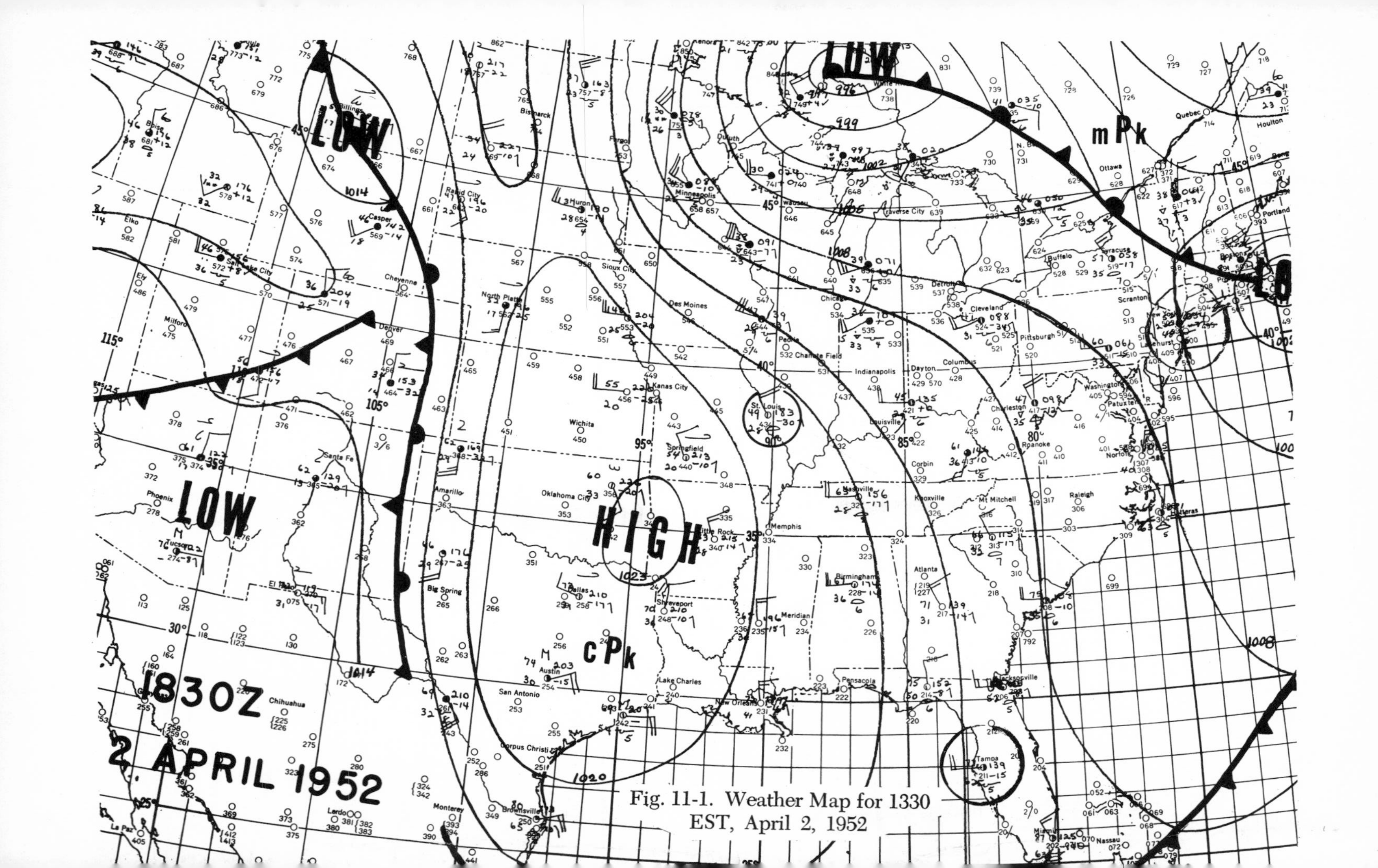

Fig. 11-1. Weather Map for 1330 EST, April 2, 1952

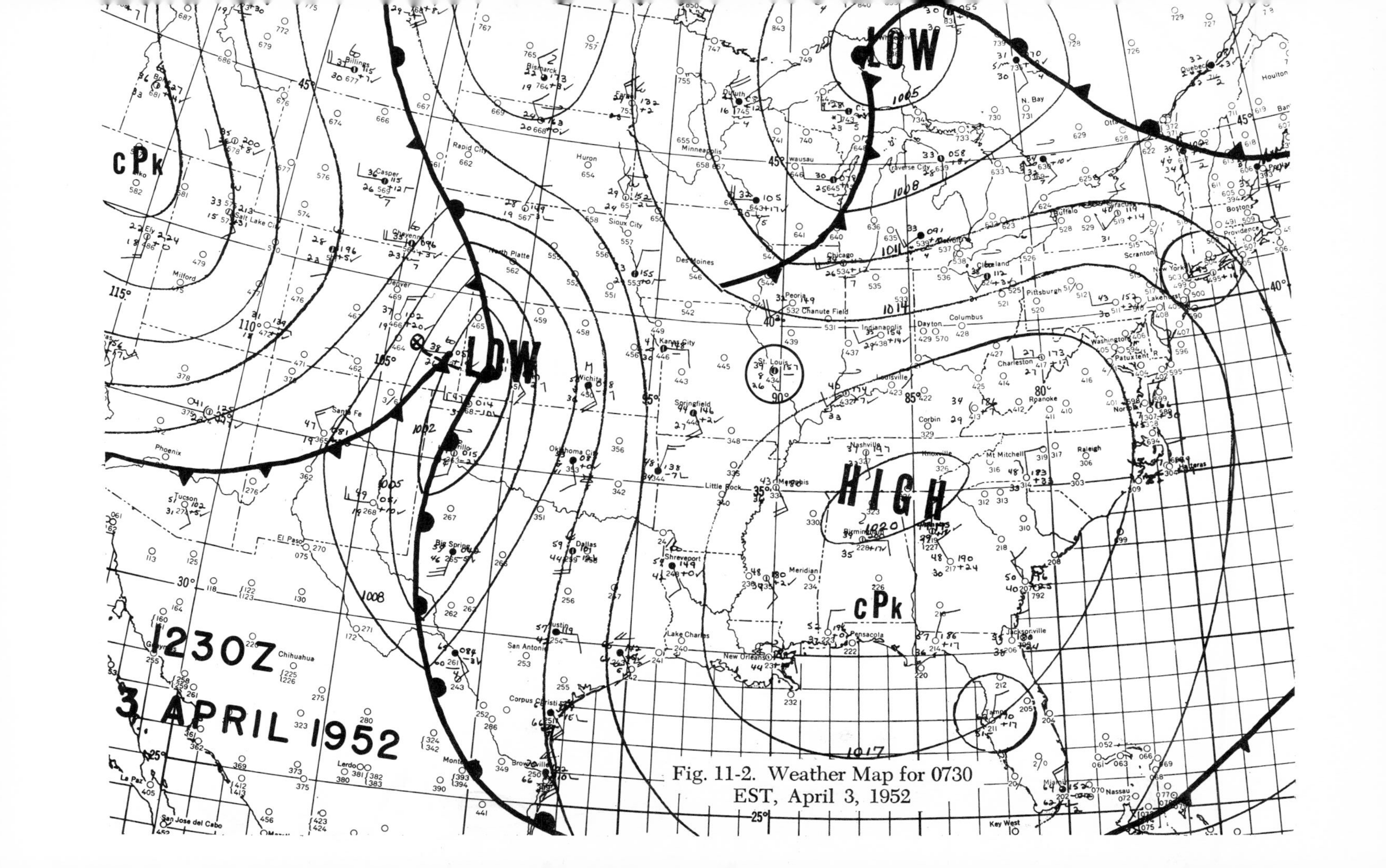

Fig. 11-2. Weather Map for 0730 EST, April 3, 1952

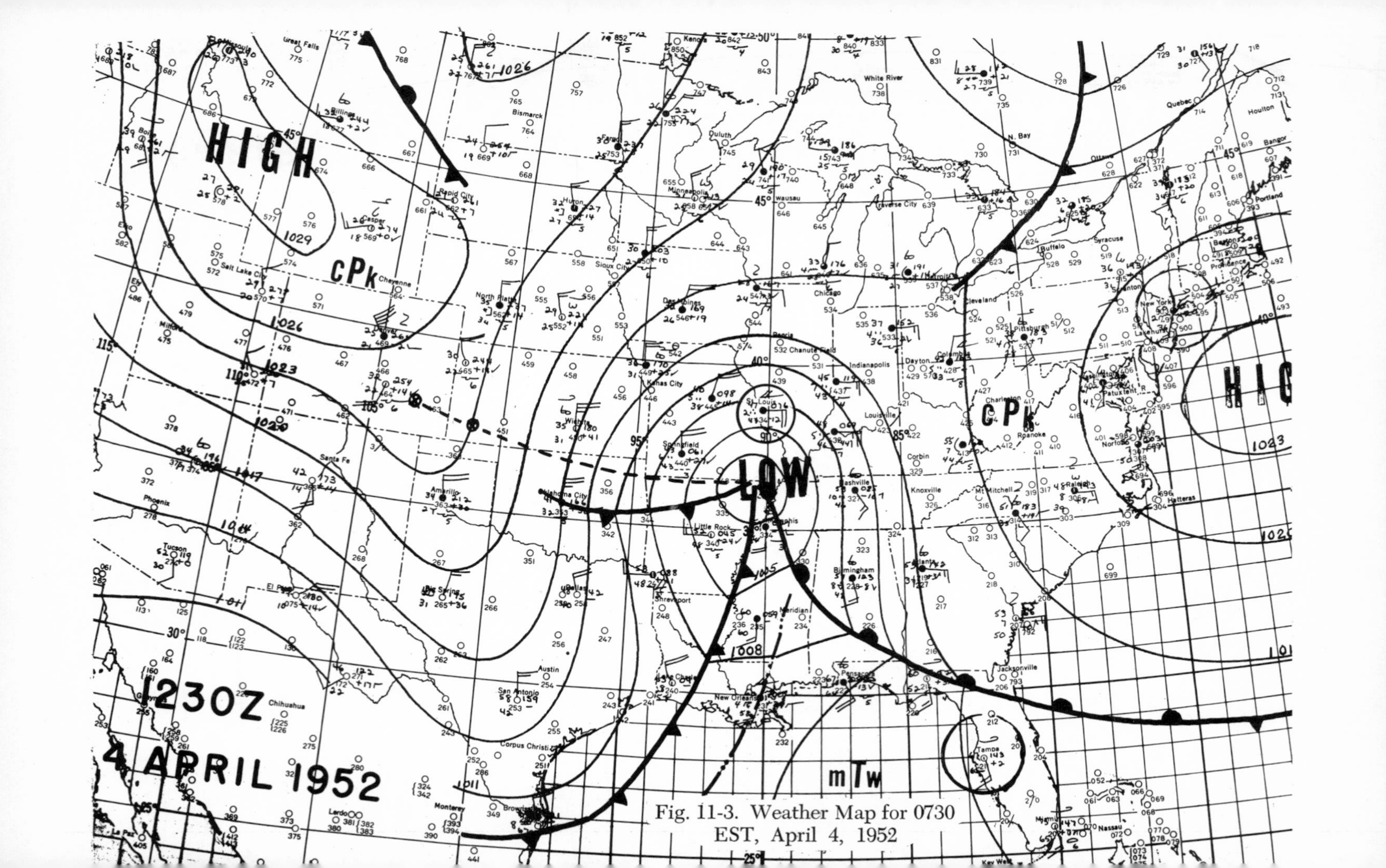

Fig. 11-3. Weather Map for 0730 EST, April 4, 1952

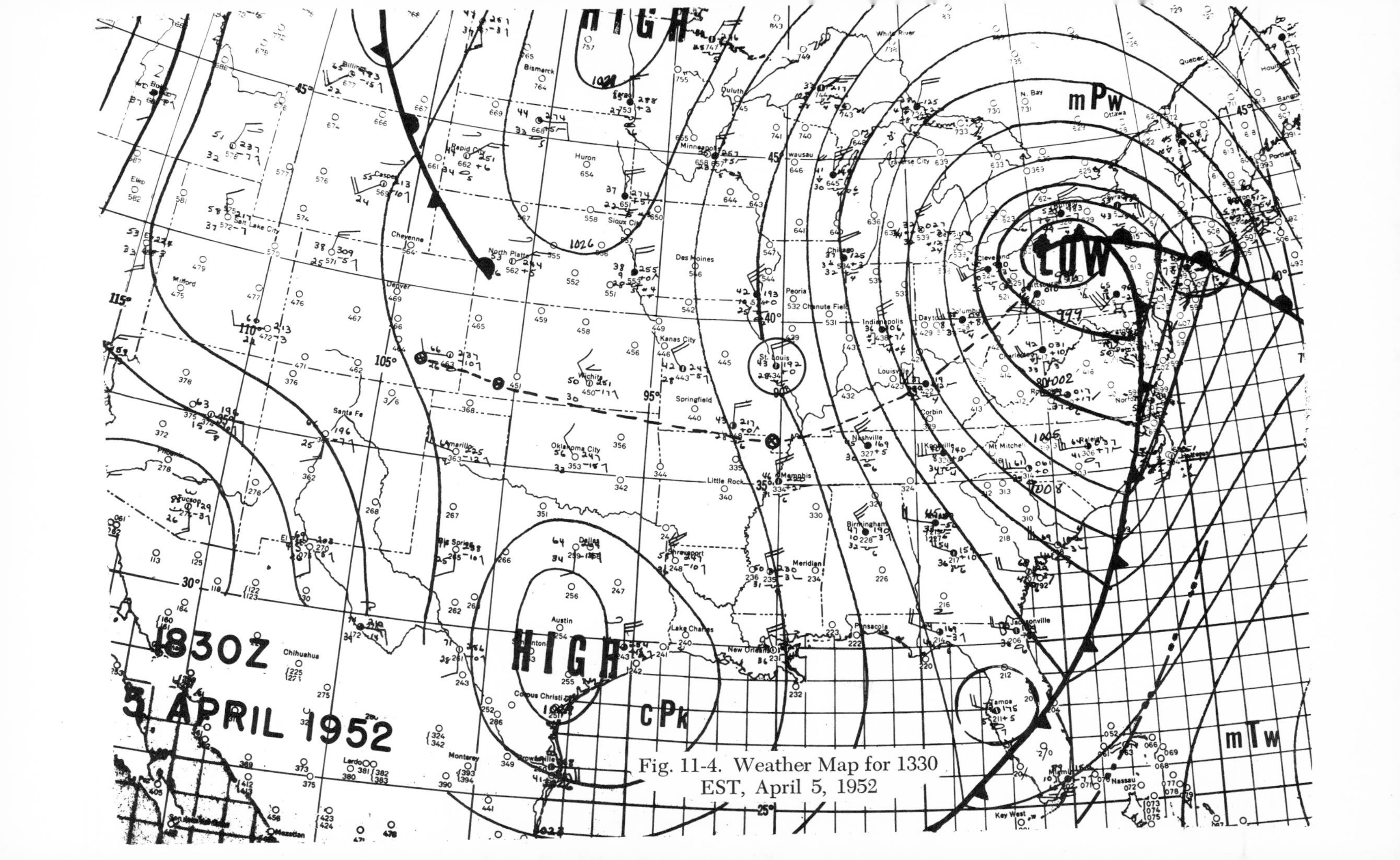

Fig. 11-4. Weather Map for 1330 EST, April 5, 1952

pattern of the eastward-moving *high*. Woods smoke, from farmers clearing their fields, was wafted over the city by the offshore breeze and settled under the temperature inversion. This gave the air a fall-like smell.

Forecasters at Tampa were continuing to enjoy *CAVU* weather, with not a cloud in the area to mar flying. Small boats roamed far offshore, and their skippers felt perfectly safe. Light winds from the land did no more than rumple the surface of the Gulf. A slight swell was left over from the 20 knot winds of yesterday, but is was long and low. It was well for the boatmen to have their fun because it was not to last long. Florida meteorologists knew that within 24 hours they would be issuing small craft warnings for the Gulf coast. These would be extended to the Atlantic coast a few hours later. The reason, of course, was the storm winding up in the Great Plains.

On the morning of April 3, St. Louis was in a "col," the neutral zone between two diagonally placed *lows* and two *highs*. Missouri was out of the circulation of one *low* (over Lake Superior) except for the northeastern corner of the state. This corner was about to be brushed by the tail end of a secondary cold front, the short but vigorous boundary of a new blast of cold air from Canada. These secondaries are often found orbiting around old occluded cyclones. Actually, they do not separate distinctly different masses, but two sections of the same air mass, each of which has undergone varying degrees of modification. Polar air that has traveled over warmer land picks up some of this warmth, and when a fresh supply of cold air follows, a secondary cold front forms between the new and the modified air. Weather in secondary fronts is less active than in the main fronts.

But the main concern of those at St. Louis was the developing storm over Kansas. During the night, the low pressure center had slipped down from Montana. It had deepened dramatically. The *cPk high* over the Rockies was showing its muscle, and the cold front of this air had plunged deep, almost to Mexico. This front was "dry" because of the lack of moisture in the air on both sides. As a matter of fact, very little weather had been stirred up by the young *low*. Weathermen knew this was temporary. As soon as wet Gulf air was sucked up into the circulation, that situation would change. So, the forecast was issued for rain and gusty winds at St. Louis. Rain was to begin during the afternoon of the third.

The wind at St. Louis was calm at 0630 CST (1230Z), April 3. There was a dense cirrus cloud cover, caused by warm air riding high over the cold dome of the *high*. The cyclone with its attendant fronts was charging eastward at 25 knots, so things would soon start popping.

About 1030, the pilot of a Mississippi River towboat, heading upriver to St. Louis with lightly loaded barges, stood on deck and cast a practiced weather eye around. His barometer had begun to fall an hour ago, and now the sky was overcast with a slate-grey alto-stratus cloud deck. Earlier he could see blue through broken cirrus clouds. He puffed on his pipe. The smoke curled swiftly away in the chill southeast wind. The air had been motionless when the boat rounded that last big bend. Now it was blowing steadily, increasing slowly. The river was beginning to be ruffled. He went back in the pilothouse wishing he could get that load into St. Louis before the wind got too strong and made steering the winding channel a chore. Fat chance, the way the weather was making up.

During the rest of the morning and early afternoon the clouds thickened and lowered. By late afternoon, a second layer had formed. These were strato-cumulus, with bases at 4,500 feet. Rain began at St. Louis at 1809 CST. The drops came fitfully at first, and were small in size, but after an hour the fall was steady. By dark, visibility was down to 5 miles, and the clouds formed a thick, amorphous layer—nimbo-stratus. The wind was gusting to 18 knots. It had backed into the east, and meteorologists knew that the low pressure center would pass to the south of St. Louis. The purple line of the barograph trace was going down steeply.

A weak warm front passed over Tampa shortly after midnight on April 4. There was no weather with it, but even the casual observer out at this late hour could tell something had happened. The faint easterly air drift, laden with woods smoke from inland, gave way to a sprightly breeze from the south. The change in air mass from *cPk* to *mTw* was apparent.

This warm front had been a cold front, though an ineffectual one, the day before. The advance edge of the *cPk high* centered over Chattanooga, it had lain east-west between Florida and Cuba. But as the *high* moved off the Atlantic coast and the midwestern *low* advanced eastward, the front was drawn back up as a warm front. It contained no weather because of the sparseness of water vapor in the air masses involved.

At 0730 EST on April 4, the icy fingers of cirrus clouds were first seen at Tampa. Snow white and delicate in appearance, they stretched across the sky, radiating from a point on the western horizon. These mares' tails looked harmless enough to the layman, but men of the shrimping fleet read the signs. They noted other signs, too. The south wind was freshening, and a long, low swell had set in from the southwest, indicating stronger winds far out in the Gulf. They knew that this was the season of the vicious squall line, and not too late for Northers.

Indeed, a Texas Norther had just entered the western Gulf of Mexico a few hours earlier, as shown in Figure 11-3. At a speed of 30 knots, the front of a cold *cPk* air mass had dashed down the plains, and was now rushing across the warm waters. Behind it were strong north winds. Out in the blue sub-tropical Gulf, crewmen of ships soon would feel the harshness of these winds and would know that winter was not yet dead. Smaller vessels pitched in the choppy waves tossed up by the wind. Seamen could smell the land, even through the sting of salt spray, and muttered, "damned Norther!"

In a wooden building at Grand Isle, Louisiana—a lonely spot on the coast to the south of New Orleans—the meteorologist for an oil company pored over the softly-glowing green disk of his radarscope. On the left of the screen, the western side, was a line of closely-grouped, bright echoes. They were aligned north-south, and moving eastward. This was the squall line. In it were many towering thunderheads reaching up to 50,000 feet. Under each was a severe downdraft with surface gusts to 40 knots. The interest of the forecaster was largely academic now. The time was 0530 CST, and he had given plenty of warning to oil rig crews offshore. They were properly buttoned down.

In Tampa, weathermen were taking a personal interest in events to the west. They, too, had spotted the squall line running ahead of the cold front. Not by radar, because it was beyond their range, but by teletype weather reports. Actually, they had anticipated it long before the first thunderstorm was reported, because such a squall line is normal. The precise atmospheric mechanics that prompt these lines of thunderstorms are not understood but, nevertheless, forecasters know where and when to look for them.

Some analysts believe the squall line, which usually runs parallel to and a hundred miles ahead of a rapidly-moving cold front, is the result of a pressure shock wave set off by the surging cold front. Something like the wave pushed ahead of a blunt-bowed barge.

At any rate, the squall line cruising eastward along the Gulf coast on the morning of April 4, 1952, was real, and it was expected to hit Tampa before midnight. A forward speed of 25 knots was projected to arrive at this estimate. But it was not only the squall line that would cause trouble.

General windiness around the deep cyclone, centered between Memphis and St. Louis on the morning of April 4, was enough to call for small craft warnings. Warnings had been up for the western Gulf since the night before, and the U. S. Weather Bureau hoisted the red pennant again at 0800 EST for the area from Cape San Blas to Key West. The advisory read, ". . . for southerly winds of 30 knots, shifting to northwest . . ."

Meanwhile, in New York, continental Polar air had been dominating the scene. During the 24-hour period from the morning of April 3 to April 4, the high pressure area moved ENE'wd from Chattanooga to a short distance off the coast, as seen in Figure 11-3. The wind at New York backed around gradually as the *high* slid by to the south, and now it was picking up from a southerly direction. This told meteorologist and seaman alike that New York was coming into the circulation of the low pressure area to the west. Cirrus clouds were beginning to appear and, by noon, as one saw the mackerel sky, a perfectly modulated alto-cumulus layer, scurrying overhead, he did not need a weather map to understand that weather was making up.

To the keen-eyed observer there were two clues to the future course of the cyclone. One was the direction from which the alto-cumulus clouds were traveling—west-southwest. This, plus the fact that the track of the *high* was of the same direction, meant that the upper level steering winds were WSW. These winds would guide the young cyclone to the ENE. It was now WSW of New York, so the storm would pass close to the city.

During the fourth, the warm front moved rapidly up the coast and ahead of it came lowering clouds and rain. The steady flow of *mTw* air riding up over this front and the backside of the Atlantic-coast *high* began to pay off. Earlier there had been no clouds or rain, but the moisture content of the warm air increased steadily as it was drawn from more remote tropical waters by the pull of the cyclone. At New York, these events happened in rapid sequence. After the alto-cumulus clouds came thick alto-stratus, then nimbostratus. By afternoon, rain was falling and the surface winds were blowing in from the sea, strong and gusty. The ocean beaches were being lashed by a healthy surf. Tumbling wind-waves rode over the tops of heavier breakers that had built up over the long fetch of open sea to the southeast. Small craft warnings were hoisted from Cape Hatteras northward. As the *low* deepened and moved inex-

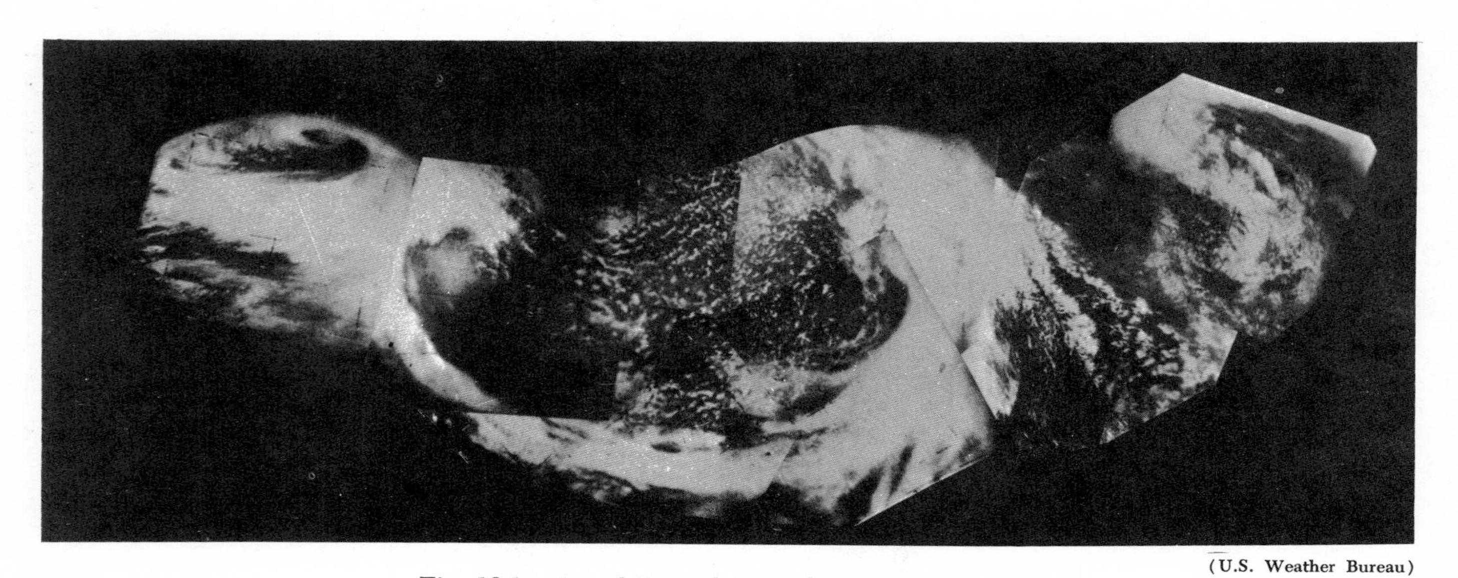

(U.S. Weather Bureau)

Fig. 12-1. Actual *Tiros* Photographs Taken on May 20, 1960

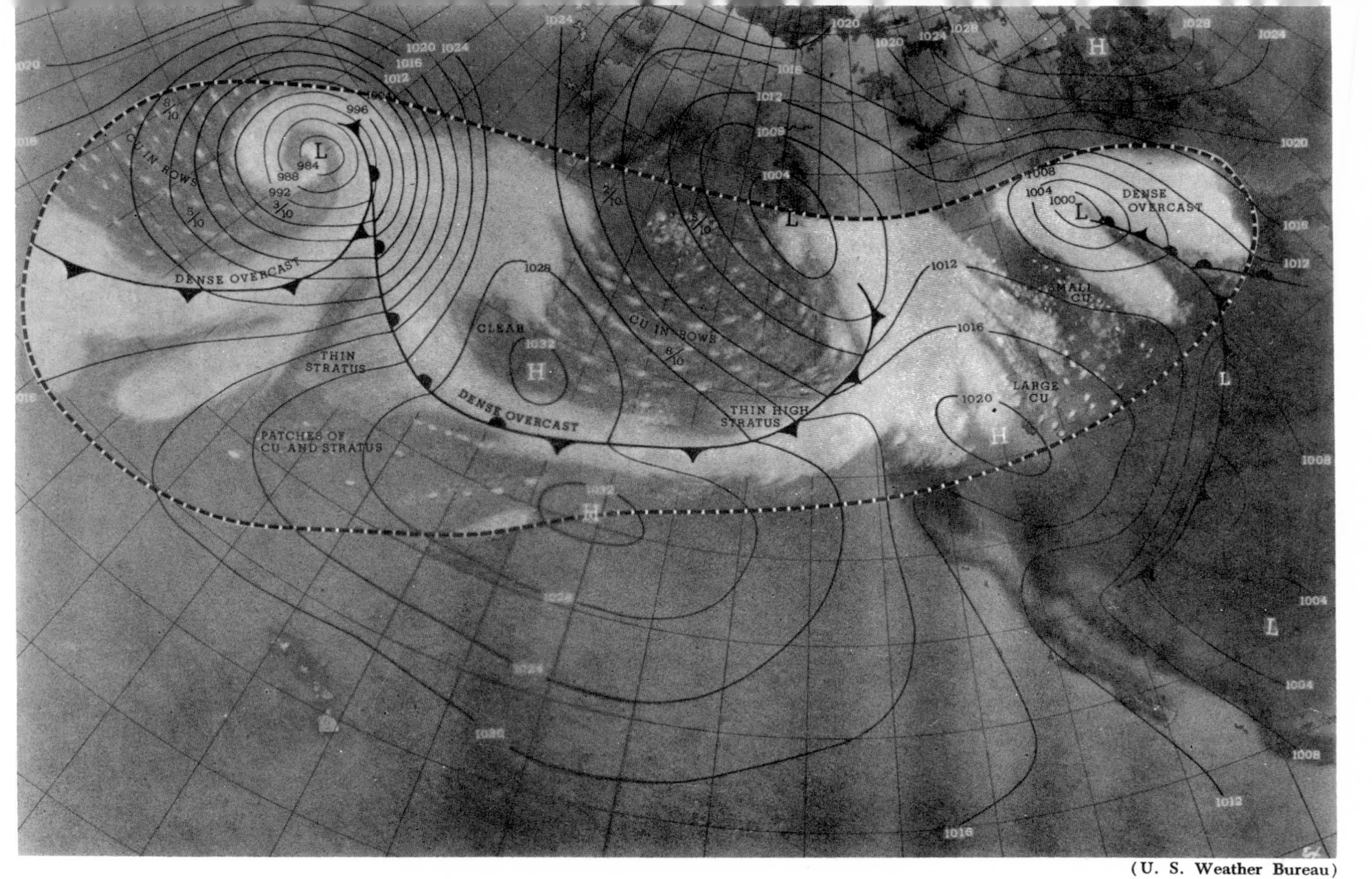

(U. S. Weather Bureau)

Fig. 12-2. Weather Map Superimposed on Cloud Pictures Taken From *Tiros* Satellite

orably toward the Atlantic, small craft warnings were extended southward to Miami. Gale warnings were issued for Cape Hatteras to Eastport.

At 0630 CST (1230Z), on April 4, St. Louis was sitting smack on top of the *low*. The barometer had gone down constantly for two days, but now it levelled and held steady at 1006.0 millibars (29.71 inches). Heavy rain, resulting from water vapor carried aloft and northward from tropical seas, fell from dark, low clouds. The east wind came in 30 knot gusts.

During the rest of the morning, the wind backed steadily and, by noon, was from due north. The meteorologist on duty in the St. Louis Weather Bureau office noted this and walked over to the barograph on his desk. The purple line, a record of atmospheric pressure, was heading up now. He knew the low pressure center had moved on, and made his forecast for clearing and colder weather. The big *cPk high* over Wyoming was cold for April. Already, the temperature at St. Louis was dropping as the wind got around to northwest. By morning, it would be near freezing.

On the southern side of the *low*, warm tropical air funneling into the center formed a wedge known as the "warm sector." The boundaries of this sector were the cold front on the west and the warm front on the east. Summerlike temperatures prevailed through Florida on the afternoon of the fourth, and dew points were in the high sixties. This fact alone identified the air mass as tropical and loaded with water vapor. So when the sharp edge of the squall line cut through this balmy air, there was plenty of action. Not as much as if the dew point temperatures in the warm air had been above 70° F., but action, nevertheless.

The squall line thunderstorms were at their worst in midafternoon. They usually are, because the warmest time of day is most conducive to the vertical convective currents that build thunderstorms. By the time the squall line reached Tampa, near midnight, the weather in it had calmed down considerably. For one thing, it had slowed to 21 knots, and the warm air was not being hit and lifted with as much force as it had been subjected to earlier.

Two hours before the squall line reached Tampa, distant lightning was seen flashing across the western horizon. Only scattered cumulus clouds hung in the tropical air of the warm sector, so the approaching thunderstorms could be seen easily. As the advancing line drew closer, there was surprisingly little change in local conditions. A little increase in wind, perhaps, but nothing else. But just before the ugly black roll cloud struck, the barometric pressure fell suddenly. The forecaster on duty in the Weather Bureau office watched the trace of the barograph take its dive with a sense of awe. He had witnessed this happening dozens of times, yet the radical drop never failed to give him a start. The wind dial on the wall made a racket as the direction indicator jumped from south to northwest and back again. The velocity hand fluctuated and then leaped up to 35 knots and hung there. The direction finally settled on northwest. Thunder boomed overhead and heavy rain pelted the windows. The barograph trace shot upward as steeply as it had fallen a few minutes ago. The squall line was there. The weatherman knew that conditions would soon return to normal and a few hours later the cold front would come. There would not be much weather with the front. Active squall lines always seem to rob following fronts of their punch. And he knew, too, that after the cold front passed, cool *cPk* air would settle over the Gulf. Then he could relax for a few days.

New York meteorologists could relax, too, but for a different reason. The real rough weather was just beginning by early evening of the fourth, but there could be no question that the *low* would plow into the Northeast. It was deepening fast and the weather would be severe for April, but all warnings were issued and nothing more could be done. Like an admiral who has committed his fleet to battle, the weatherman who has issued a correct forecast—no matter how bad the weather—can only sit back and watch the show.

The storm did, indeed, plow through the Northeast. New York went through a 20-hour period of pre-warm frontal rain, fog and onshore winds. At 1330 EST (1830Z), April 5 (Figure 11-4), the warm front passed. The rain stopped, the clouds broke, and a balmy south wind relieved the easterly gales. Along the beaches, the rash of wind-waves disappeared but the heavier sea swell continued to attack the shore with booming breakers. They came in from the southeast. It was a pleasant respite, but was doomed to a short stay because the cold front was close by. Then came the cold northwest winds pouring *cPk* air into the area.

At this point, the cyclone reached the zenith of its intensity with a central pressure of 995.0 millibars (29.28 inches). The occlusion process had begun, and so began the slow, agonizing death of the storm. Winter, in the form of cold Polar air, again spread throughout the nation. But it did not stay long, for the warm sun of April soon modified the air mass to a tolerable degree.

Meteorologists would forecast other such cyclones, but small craft sailors knew this: with each passing day, climatology was on their side and there would shortly come a time when fitting out could be postponed no longer. Then the counterclockwise flow around migratory *lows* would mean nothing more serious than good sailing winds. Until the following October, that is.

The weather map series for April, 1952, can be considered typical of late winter and early spring. But meteorologists know only too well that, at times, the weather exasperatingly refuses to fit the seasons and weather maps, in the irrepressible fashion, form their own patterns without regard to man's wishes.

For example, a conventional fall and winter feature is the Gulf *low,* a cyclone that swings up from the Gulf of Mexico through the Southeast, accompanied by thoroughly nasty weather. Off Cape Hatteras, the *low* winds up into a real storm, often with hurricane-force winds.

In season, Gulf *lows* move on their courses as regular as ferry-boats. But, not infrequently, a year will pass without the first such cyclone occurring. That causes weathermen to tear their hair, especially when all signs point to formation. This illustrates a point, once again. Even though weather is stereotyped for the purpose of teaching it, in actual practice anything can happen. That is why forecasters can't win 'em all.

Chapter 4

Clouds, Nature's Majestic Signposts

For countless centuries, since the earth has had an atmosphere, clouds have crossed the skies in recognizable shapes and patterns. The typhoon that destroyed Kublai Khan's invasion fleet off the coast of Japan in the year 1281 was, no doubt, heralded by radiating cirrus and cirro-cumulus clouds identical to those we see today. The fierce Blackbeard, westing down the trades in *Queen Anne's Revenge,* looking for a Spanish prize, sailed under tropical cumulus that any present-day sailor would know.

How is it that bits of moisture, day in and day out, mold themselves into familiar forms? Why doesn't moisture just condense into characterless masses of mist? When we consider that clouds are made up simply of small water droplets, like steam, or of ice crystals if cold enough, then it is remarkable that these clouds can be classed into certain standard types that appear the same the world over.

Artists, however skilled, always have and probably always will depict clouds as shapeless blobs of color. Even marine artists, who lovingly detail the finer points of the ships and seascapes they paint, never seem to catch clouds on their canvases that remotely resemble the real thing. Too bad, because clouds are such a vital part of sea scenes.

Clouds are Forecasters

Artists and landlubbers might think of clouds as meaningless blotches that mar the blue of the sky, but sailors know better. Seafaring men long ago learned to read the messages of nature's signposts in the sky and to forecast the changing environment with surprising accuracy. Seamen have never thought of clouds as mere accumulations of water vapor, but as fascinating things of beauty—sometimes mysterious, sometimes ominous, but always as harbingers of the weather that is so important to them.

Whether the form of the clouds is that of feathery cirrus plumes flying silently overhead, or fleecy cumulus wandering around on a summer day, or leaden strato-cumulus driving hell-bent across a winter sky, sailors know that each has its meaning, each brings its weather, each has its reason for being. And that is the important lesson to be learned by all who "do business in great waters," whether they "go down to the sea" for a week end or for a lifetime.

Cloud Classifications

So that weather observers around the globe can standardize their cloud observation reports, the World Meteorological Organization, with headquarters in Geneva, Switzerland, has issued a monumental book, the *International Cloud Atlas*. This beautiful work contains 78 photographs of the many cloud types and a complete breakdown of the Latin terms in use to describe clouds. The scheme for classifying clouds by Latin names goes back to 1803, when it was devised by an Englishman, Luke Howard.

If you know Latin, the whole thing makes sense, because the terms actually describe the clouds' appearance. For example, cirrus, "a lock of hair;" cumulus, "an accumulation, a heap;" stratus, "to spread or flatten out." But if you do not understand Latin, be not despaired. The system is easy to learn. Well, not the entire system, because when the international meteorologists gathered a few years ago, they took care of every possible eventuality, down to exotic supplementary and accessory cloud types that may never be seen by most observers. Let us go through the delineation of cloud families and genera first, then explain how each cloud is formed and what it means to the man on deck.

The Four Families. The altitudes at which clouds form is not mere happenstance. It is so important, as a matter of fact, that the four cloud families are specified with height as the criterion. Almost as if they were in different atmospheres, the clouds of each family are usually divorced from each other. Of course, at times the families merge into one glorious mass, or mess, as in a warm front. The fourth family type allows for clouds that extend vertically through all levels.

High Family. Clouds of this family are cirrus, cirro-stratus, and cirro-cumulus. They exist above 20,000 feet. In Polar regions, they may be lower.

Middle Family. At heights from 6,500 feet to 20,000 feet, the middle clouds, alto-cumulus and alto-stratus, are the most portentous of all. They indicate countercurrents of moist air, and usually mean that lower, and more active, clouds are nearby.

Low Family. Low clouds are based from ground up to 6,500 feet. They are indicative, not so much of what is to come, but of that which is already here. More likely than not, they result from influences of the immediate vicinity and not from some distant storm area, as in the case of high and middle clouds. Cumulus, stratus, strato-cumulus, and nimbo-stratus (although this one is often put in the middle group) belong.

Low-With-Vertical Development Family. Since cumulo-nimbus clouds begin near the ground, but extend to great heights, a special family tree had to be created to take care of this cloud type. The cumulo-nimbus is only one cloud, no matter how high it goes.

The Ten Genera. These are the old familiar standbys, the same as mentioned above.

Cirrus. Detached, delicate, and snow-white, it is fibrous, and arranged in patches or narrow bands. Cirrus has no shading and casts no shadows. It is the "mare's tail" of proverb fame and each plume is hooked or tufted on the ends, as befits a proper mare's tail.

Cirro-cumulus. Obviously disturbed by high level turbulence, this cloud is made up of little balls, or ripples, in uniform lines much like the ribbed lines of sand on a beach. Cirro-cumulus is in a constant state of change and seldom lasts for long. This is "mackerel sky," the companion to mares' tails.

Cirro-stratus. A transparent, whitish veil of cloud, often covering the sky and usually producing haloes. As it thickens and lowers, cirro-stratus sometimes goes into alto-stratus. At this point, the cloud layer develops a dark shading.

Alto-cumulus. A sort of big brother to cirro-cumulus, this middle cloud also passes for mackerel sky. The cloud globules or ribbed bands are larger, however, and often are shaded. Alto-cumulus is a cloud of many faces, or species, as the *Atlas* calls them, and each has its meaning.

Alto-stratus. A greyish or bluish sheet, occasionally striated or fibrous, but normally smooth in appearance. In its early stages, the sun or moon shines weakly through the layer, as through ground glass. This is the "watery sun" that is said to have "rain in its eye." It usually does.

Cumulus. The well-known "cotton puff" clouds of summer. Cumulus clouds occur at all seasons, of course, but they are more

Fig. 13-1. Top Left: Cirrus. Fig. 13-2. Top Right: Cirro-cumulus. Fig. 13-3. Bottom Left: Cirro-stratus. Fig. 13-4. Bottom Right: Alto-cumulus.

Fig. 13-5. Top Left: Alto-stratus. Fig. 13-6. Top Right: Cumulus. Fig. 13-7. Bottom Left: Strato-cumulus. Fig. 13-8. Bottom Right: Nimbo-stratus.

frequent in warm weather. These are flat-bottomed, with rounded, bulging tops. They vary from "humilis" (small fair-weather cumulus) to "calvus" (huge, towering rain clouds), and are, without question, the most beautiful clouds in the sky.

Strato-cumulus. Similar to stratus, but slightly higher. The base is more sharply defined and it has an uneven, "rolling" structure. This, too, is a "dry" cloud, without appreciable precipitation.

Nimbo-stratus. The orphan in the families of clouds. It cannot decide to which family it belongs, but the choice is narrowed down to "low" and "middle." By definition, precipitation must be falling continuously from it, although the basic cloud type might be alto-stratus, or a lower layer. At any rate, nimbo-stratus is a heavy, grey sheet.

Stratus. Low, light grey, and "foggy" looking. Sometimes ragged, sometimes smooth. This is a non-precipitating cloud, except for some occasional light drizzle.

Cumulo-nimbus. The ultimate in cloud development, the thunderhead. This is the overgrown cumulus cloud that contains a thunderstorm. Its base is near the ground, but the top is higher than 25,000 feet and may reach 70,000 feet, on occasions.

It is fine to know cloud families and genera. It is necessary in order to make identification, but the sailor is concerned with only one thing: What does it all mean to him? After the clouds have been identified, then what?

How Clouds Form

Clouds, like the red rash of chicken pox, are visible symptoms of something more profound going on. As we said, clouds are simply masses of condensed moisture. But how did this moisture become condensed? It can happen in only two ways. Air, with invisible water vapor therein, must be lifted, and thereby cooled, until the vapor condenses; or there must be horizontal countercurrents of air of different temperatures. By contact, the warmer air is cooled and, presto, clouds form.

This brings us to a question asked at the beginning of this chapter. Why do clouds repeatedly form in familiar patterns? Atmospheric processes repeat themselves, year after year, and clouds are visible evidence that this is so. This fact makes them valuable as bellwethers. They tip off the master pattern of air flow at all levels—invisible, but very real.

Fig. 13-9. Stratus

Fig. 13-10. Cumulo-nimbus

When man took to the air and began milling around in the realm of the clouds, some of the romance and mystery was swept away. Clouds, when flown through, lose much of their beauty and individuality. From the inside, they look like so much grey steam. It is the old story of familiarity and contempt. But not until recently, with the advent of jet aircraft, was the previously inaccessible cirrus level invaded. Now, thousands of grandmothers annually fly through cirrus clouds. Most of them probably never notice the smoky, white ice crystals whisking by the cabin window, and they think little of the brief, sharp bumpiness as the plane goes through the cirrus. Certainly, the passengers aboard the jet airliner are unaware that the mild turbulence is at the "shear-edge" of two distinct layers of air, one overriding the other, and as cleanly separated as the blades on a pair of closing shears.

Far below, some weatherwise groundling gazing aloft might not understand about the shear-edge, either, but he knows something is going on up there where the grandmothers are tooling along at 350 knots. And he is right. Something is going on.

A strong west wind at 28,000 feet is sliding over a less-strong northwest flow of air. The lower layer is cold and dry. The upper flow is a few degrees warmer and, what is more important, more moist. This west wind, tearing along at 80 knots, has just come from over an active low pressure area several hundred miles away. It has picked up moisture carried aloft by the storm and, as it cuts over the top of the colder air, it is cooled by contact. This condenses the invisible moisture into ice crystals. The ice-crystal clouds, cirrus, are formed in long, narrow bands. They are striated, fibrous, and aligned in the direction of the wind. Their distended shape leaves no doubt that strong winds are rampant up there. Remember, this wind is coming from the storm area, so the cirrus fingers point from that direction. The ends of the cloud streaks become hooked or tufted when they venture into the opposing air flow and these hooks clearly show the change in wind direction.

Moisture is sparse in these thin, cold upper reaches, so when the small amount of moisture present condenses, clouds are sparse, too. That is why cirrus are transparent, flimsy and, in themselves, completely harmless. Cirrus clouds are always made of ice crystals. Even over the hottest land on earth, it is virtually impossible to have above-freezing temperatures at 20,000 feet.

Modern cirrus-cloud watchers have an extra complication tossed in that never concerned ancient mariners. That is, condensation trails from high flying aircraft. Hot exhaust gases, containing quite a lot of water vapor, expand greatly upon leaving the engine, and this aids in condensing the moisture directly into ice crystals. A plane, otherwise invisible because of great altitudes, makes a good target when followed by several miles of shining white tail. Because of this, military meteorologists have long had an interest in "contrails," and forecast the altitudes at which they are most likely to appear. Generally, contrails form in air whose temperature is colder than −38° C., and whose humidity is more than 40 percent.

Cirro-cumulus are formed in much the same way as cirrus, but indicate a greater degree of instability between the two shearing wind flows. Hence, the boiling, bubbling character of the cloud layer. One situation that would cause this is to reverse the order of the two wind currents mentioned in cirrus formation. Instead of the warmer air running over cold, have the colder wind, from northwest, swooping down over the top of a west or southwest flow. The colder air, being heavier, tumbles down through the warmer layer, resulting in cloud "bundles."

Of late, however, meteorologists have learned that cirro-cumulus clouds are more often associated with the jet stream. The location of the jet stream was discernable in *Tiros* weather satellite pictures by the bands of cirrus clouds following it. Along the edges of this monstrous "river of air," turbulence and eddies are rampant. This turbulence has, at times, caused serious trouble for jet aircraft. And it is well established that wherever the jet stream meanders, low pressure areas pop up more easily. So, the old salts and their mackerel sky were on firm ground, if such can be said of a deepwater man on the rolling deck of a sailing ship.

Unlike cirrus and cirro-cumulus, cirro-stratus is a smooth sheet of ice crystals covering a large area. There is a reason for this. The method of formation is different. In cirro-stratus, condensation of vapor occurs by gentle lifting of the air rather than by contact cooling. This lifting is accomplished by warmer air climbing over the top of a cold, heavier air mass. The upslope motion is slow and easy, so the cirro-stratus deck is stable.

If this talk of "warmer air riding over . . ." and upslope motion sounds familiar, recall that the same expressions were used in discussing warm fronts in Chapter 2. Indeed, what we are describing is the *avant-garde* of the warm front, the high level beginning of overrunning that will lower away until the encroaching warm air sweeps even the ground clean of cold air. So, you see, a cirro-stratus sheet is worthy of all honors bestowed on it as a precursor of ill tidings. This is especially true if it thickens and lowers steadily.

Meteorologists try to grab a firm purchase on the elements and avoid the use of too many "maybe's," and "on the other hands." But it is no secret that these elements are elastic and elusive, and refuse to be stereotyped. So to say that cirro-stratus clouds—or mackerel sky and mares' tails—always indicate a need for "tall ships to carry short sails" is wrong. There will be times when these clouds will disappear as fast as they appeared because of changes in upper level wind patterns.

Another exception concerning cirrus is found in the tropics, as well as during summer in the mid-latitudes. Frequently the sky is a riot of cirro-stratus and cirrus, resulting from the spreading out of the tops of big thunderstorms. These cirrus will gradually thin out to nothing—until the next afternoon, when they will blossom forth again.

When a warm front approaches and the overrunning gets lower, the cirro-stratus deck will change into alto-stratus, mostly by virtue of going below the bottom limit of cirro-form clouds. But other changes take place that cause alto-stratus to be a different cloud altogether. It is thicker and darker and has more substance simply because it is in warmer, denser air—air than can hold more water vapor. This is evident by its greyish or bluish color as contrasted with thin, white cirro-stratus. While still fairly high, alto-stratus allows the sun to shine weakly through, but, as it lowers, the sun is blotted out by the increased moisture. By the time this happens, there is enough water vapor for rain. It falls first as virga, rain streamers that evaporate in mid-air, but soon the air becomes loaded and the falling drops reach the ground. Alto-stratus rain (or snow, or sleet) is light and steady. It expresses the character of the cloud itself: smooth, stable, and extensive.

A high degree of confidence can be placed on alto-stratus as a rain predictor. Even so, it, too, can sound a false alarm. The overrunning warm air can be cut off suddenly by an upper level pressure trough moving through. Like cirro-stratus, alto-stratus can come from the spreading out of thunderstorm tops. This variety, cumulonimbo-genitus, dissipates in a short while.

There are times when it is difficult to tell alto-cumulus from cirro-cumulus, so similar do they appear. One way is that of shading. Cirro-cumulus has no shading, but alto-cumulus does, except for unusually thin layers. Another test is to compare the individual cloud globules with the little finger held at arm's length. If the cloud elements are larger than the finger's width, they are not cirro-cumulus.

Alto-cumulus clouds come in assorted forms, but they all have one thing in common. They result from conflicting horizontal air currents in the middle level. One, or both, of the air masses must be unstable, else the clouds would be thin alto-stratus. Precipitation does not usually fall from alto-cumulus because it is a thin layer, but often the layer thickens to become undulated alto-stratus, and then comes the rain.

Alto-cumulus undulatus, the wavy, banded kind, quite obviously results from a horizontal wind shear in which an organized wave pattern is set up by the overrunning air. This has no great significance except to point up the mild instability at the shear level. Incidentally, the waves, or billows, result from the up and down air motion in the wave pattern. Upward moving air cools and condenses to build billows, while air flowing downward is warmed slightly and dissipates the clouds. Hence, the clear streaks.

There are other brands, namely alto-cumulus floccus and castellanus (everybody but the editors of the *International Cloud Atlas* call it castellatus) that bear watching. In these, the cloud elements look like miniature cumulus turrets, indicating very unstable air in the middle levels. If these types are seen in the morning, thunderstorms are almost a certainty by afternoon.

Middle clouds are the most significant of all. They display changes in the atmosphere close enough to affect those doing the viewing, but from sources far enough away to have import over a large area. High clouds do somewhat the same job, but occasionally their reason for being is a bit remote from the earthbound.

One final word on middle clouds. They are often portentous, but, at times, they appear after the fact. Following a frontal passage, for instance, alto-cumulus and alto-stratus may be present, and may hang on for many hours, but this does not mean that the front will turn around and come back (however, fronts do this, sometimes). So, the thumb rule is: if middle clouds appear during good weather, expect trouble; if they are present following bad weather, look for more improvement.

By the way, you can have your own cloud atlas for thirty cents. Ask for Circular "S", *Manual of Cloud Forms,* from the Superintendent of Documents, Washington 25, D. C. It is well worth the price.

Several years ago, nimbus was a recognized cloud type. It was considered to be a rain cloud then, and is now, but in present usage it is combined with either stratus or cumulus. Nimbo-stratus is a stable layer cloud, formed by extensive horizontal countercurrents of wind. It can be above or below the 6,500-foot level, the dividing line between middle and low clouds. It is usually thought of as a low cloud because, in a nimbo-stratus rain situation, found more often than not in winter, the rain falls continuously for a long time and this so saturates the air that another low-level cloud deck is fashioned. Actually, the rain is coming down through these low clouds, but it is impossible to tell that by looking at it.

Clouds must have real substance to generate rain—even light rain, but especially the all-day downpour of nimbo-stratus weather. The layer must be several thousands of feet thick and fed by a continuous input of moist air overrunning cooler air. And that is the difference between nimbo-stratus and stratus.

Stratus does not have this depth. It often looks rainy, but is no more than a high fog. Classical stratus is found on the California coast in summer. Warm, fairly damp winds blowing in from the Pacific are chilled by the cold waters near the coast. This sometimes results in sea fog, but if the wind is vigorous, as it normally is, a stratus deck spreads over the coast. The layer is thin and burns off soon after the sun's heat takes effect.

Strato-cumulus lends itself to generalities perhaps less than any other cloud. It is ubiquitous. Wherever there is wind over the surface and the air is damp, there is strato-cumulus. Its very name indicates an "all-purpose" type, comprising horizontal as well as vertical characteristics. The best explanation for this layer-like cloud is that it is built by horizontal air flow, but the air must have a degree of instability, allowing some vertical motion. The wind "rolls" over the ground or water surface in large wind waves. At times, the top of each wave is a cloud roll. At other times, the rolling motion is more disorganized and the cloud base reflects this.

Most strato-cumulus is caused by this action, although there are some varieties that differ. One, strato-cumulus cumulo-genitus, to get back to Mr. Howard's Latin, spreads out from cumulus clouds that have gone stable. This kind does not last long.

To meteorologists, strato-cumulus is certainly the most exasperating of all cloud types. It has a way of popping up in a matter of minutes to cover the sky with a heavy, dull overcast. The day may begin bright and clear only to have a low ceiling sweep in by midmorning. This plays havoc with temperature forecasts, because it usually happens in cold weather when the difference in daily maximum temperature may be 20 degrees, depending upon whether or not the sun shines.

Strato-cumulus is not a rain cloud because it is caused by "ground wind" and lacks substance for precipitation. But, if there should be doubt because of its dreary appearance, check these "no rain" points:

- Did the cloud deck move in under a clear sky, or under harmless high clouds?
- Can you see blue sky through the breaks?

Cumulus clouds are the moisture caps to vertical air currents. Their bulging white tops outline the advance edge of the rising air and their flat bottoms show the level at which the upward-moving air becomes saturated, due to expansional cooling. Cumulus are strictly local clouds. They herald no distant weather; they tell of no meteorological event other than that which is to happen to the clouds themselves. But, even if they do not have far-reaching implications, cumulus are important, because weather that vitally affects the boatman can come from them. Rain showers, squalls, waterspouts, even tornadoes, can develop in a few short hours from puff ball cumulus.

So the man in the boat will do well to cultivate a familiarity with cumulus. Watch them grow, note how fast they build, observe their structure, get to know how their tops look under various conditions. For it is the tops that give most of the clues.

All cumulus begin as "fair weather cumulus," the popular name for cumulus humilis. That is not to detract from the term fair weather cumulus—it is a valid name. But genuine fair weather cumulus remain in their elemental form all afternoon, without building, whereas cumulus destined for bigger things (like thunderstorms) continue to grow. Humilis do not grow because the upcurrents are weak and taper off a couple of thousand feet up. The air is stable except for the very lowest layer which has been given a bit of instability by the sun's heating of the ground.

Forecasters can tell when conditions are ripe for cumulus to build into showers and thunderstorms by consulting the pseudo-adiabatic chart. Remember, on this chart is plotted the temperature lapse rate as obtained daily by sending radiosonde balloons aloft. If the temperature drops off rapidly upward, and if there is sufficient moisture in the air, then convective showers are forecast.

The cloud watcher has only a slight disadvantage over the meteorologist, however, because he can tell by the appearance of the cumulus what the conditions of stability and moisture are.

The average height of cumulus bottoms is about 2,500 feet. Lower bases indicate that the air mass moisture content is high, and vice versa. If the cloud builds rapidly upward, the air is unstable and the updrafts needed to produce thunderstorms are present. Hard, well-defined edges to the cloud top show that these updrafts mean business and are pushing eagerly. The snow-white, cauliflower-like bulges and turrets of building cumulus show, too, that the air's water content is high. Under these conditions, expect showers soon.

If either available water vapor or instability is lacking, nothing will happen except to have a sky full of pretty clouds. When updrafts are virile, but moisture is sparse, cumulus tops will build, but they appear ragged and soft. Even more dramatic evidence of dryness is the "burning off" of turrets. Otherwise, healthy looking turrets will separate from the cumulus cloud and, in a matter of minutes, thin out and disappear. When this happens, the chances of showers are slim.

Often, moisture is plentiful but the instability that encouraged cumulus to develop extends only so high. Then the cloud flattens and ceases to shoot upward. A premature anvil, of sorts, is formed but, unless rain has already begun in the cloud, there will not be any action.

To say just when a cumulus cloud becomes a cumulo-nimbus is difficult. The *Cloud Atlas* explains that a large cumulus changes into cumulo-nimbus when the top loses its sharp edges, and a fibrous anvil forms. Lightning, thunder, or hail coming from the cloud also qualifies it as cumulo-nimbus. A mere rain shower does not.

Cumulo-nimbus can build from cumulus to form "air mass" thunderstorms. They can result when air is mechanically lifted by the wedge of a cold front, or by air flowing up a mountain side. They also can come from the terrific dynamic lifting of air in a squall line, and this is the biggest and most violent kind of cumulo-nimbus. The mechanics of thunderstorm clouds is covered in detail in Chapter 5.

Man has been tampering with clouds for some time now, trying to wring rain from them; trying to dry them up; trying to twist them out of recognizable shape. The Indians built bonfires and later experimenters have thrown silver iodide crystals, water, salt, Dry Ice, lampblack, and what-have-you into nature's frail, yet potent, monuments of mist. So far, nothing has changed clouds from their time-honored forms. We hope nothing ever will.

Chapter 5

Squall!

It is little wonder than many young sailors develop complexes about squalls before they have graduated from the rowboat class. Parents of these neophyte skippers are often heard to deliver safety lectures about the hazards to be found out on the briny deep of the sheltered sound. Inevitably, a final warning is included: "... and watch out for squalls."

Perhaps most junior mariners (some senior ones, too) do not understand just exactly what constitutes a squall. Apprehensive hours are spent each summer by boatmen searching cloudless skies, "watching out for squalls." The idea seems to be afoot that squalls, like sea serpents of old, might at any time come swooping down to gobble up unsuspecting seamen.

The ability to recognize a squall in the making and size it up for intensity and direction of movement can give comfort to week-end sailors—many of whom possess genuine sea legs, and can tie rolling half hitches in their sleep, but who are not quite sure of the mechanics of a squall.

What Causes a Squall?

What is a squall? Webster's Dictionary and the Meteorological Glossary agree that it is a "brief, violent windstorm, usually, but not necessarily, with rain or snow." It might be well first to polish off those windstorms that appear to qualify as squalls because of their "brief, violent" characteristics, but that do not really belong to the local rainstorm family that is the crux of the problem for yachtsmen. It is true that sudden, strong winds do spring up for no apparent reason, but actually there always is a reason. Their cause almost always can be found on the daily weather map and, hence, they can be forecast. Such dry coastal winds as the *Santa Ana* of California and the *Tehuantipecer* of Mexico, though they may strike with exasperating suddenness, can be anticipated in advance for hours—even days. Weathermen know when conditions are ripe by the build-up of air pressure on the inland side of mountain passes and, when this pressure has reached a certain point, the air gushes through the pass like water through a sluice.

Local boatmen are not likely to be caught off guard by such winds, though. Neither are yachtsmen of the Texas and Louisiana coasts likely to be cruising far offshore when a Norther spreads out over the blue waters of the Gulf of Mexico. Even if the U. S. Weather Bureau did not have small craft warnings hoisted, which it always does for such occasions, weatherwise sailors of the area can smell the cold front approaching and head in before the strong, cold winds sweep down from the plains.

On the subject of cold fronts, we are getting closer to squalls, for it is well known that the two go hand-in-hand. So much so, in fact, that in the days before the nature of fronts was understood (not as far back as one may think), cold fronts were often called line squalls, on the assumption that, through some mysterious process, a squall cloud had aligned itself into a long and well-defined front. There is such a thing as a squall line, but cold fronts and squall lines are discussed later in this chapter. Right now, a thorough understanding should be achieved of the makeup of the lone, isolated squall cloud.

In most cases, a squall is a thunderstorm. It is that simple. The wind comes from a cumulo-nimbus cloud. The exception is the big rain cloud that has not built up quite enough in height to reach thunderstorm proportions, but still packs a wallop in its downdraft. And it is that downdraft that is the squall, the sudden wind. In order to contain a downdraft wind, the cloud must have considerable vertical development. No matter how black, how ugly a cloud may appear, it will not be harmful unless it pokes its nose straight up into the atmosphere for several miles—at least 25,000 feet. The real jib-rippers range up to 40,000 to 60,000 feet.

Then, when the heavy, cold air comes charging down through the cloud, it has plenty of room to gather speed and spread out into a severe first gust, or "squall front," that can bowl over unprepared boaters (Figure 14).

Why the downdraft? To reverse an old saying, that which comes down had first to go up. Sir Isaac Newton might shudder at such a premise, but it is true enough in the case of squall clouds. The cloud is built by ascending warm air. After this air has reached high altitudes and has lost its upward momentum, it is cold and dense.

Triggered off by falling rain, it wooshes earthward. At first, the descending air is only a cold core within the cloud, but finally it consumes the entire cloud and succeeds in demolishing it.

Following a Squall Cloud from Birth to Dissipation

Let us follow a typical squall cloud from its birth as a small puff-ball cumulus through to the dissipation stage. Total life: three hours.

We will assume that it is early on a pleasant summer afternoon and we are cruising northward up Chesapeake Bay. The sky is mostly clear, but here and there lazily hang little white clouds, much like puffs of cotton pinned to the azure-blue cloth of the sky. A light southeasterly breeze ripples the water. A casual observer might dismiss the weather as beyond reproach. After all, the forecast had mentioned that only "widely scattered afternoon thundershowers" would mar the day. But we have had other experiences with those summer afternoon thundershowers and are a bit suspicious of any cumulus cloud that builds too fast. And that one over the land to the west—it must be fifteen miles away—has grown vigorously during the past twenty minutes. It is being fed by a strong, rising hot air current, probably from a large plowed field. An airplane flying under the cloud would experience a sharp bump.

The top of the cumulus cloud is snow-white and has a round, hard appearance, much like the head of a cauliflower. The air beneath the cloud is clear, evidence that no rain is falling. There is, no doubt, rain within the cloud, but all air currents are updrafts at this time and the water drops are suspended, tumbling, unable to fall. By now, the cloud has reached a height of 25,000 feet and is drifting eastward. It is roughly six miles away and appears to be on a collision course with us.

Suddenly, the bottom seems to drop out of the cloud and a dark curtain of rain falls to the ground. The cloud now has a downdraft and a squall, or gust, of wind. That gust is not very strong yet—say, 25 knots—but it will build steadily during the next half-hour. A minute or so later, a loud clap of thunder reverberates over the green waters of the Bay. The cumulus cloud is officially a thunderstorm as of this moment. It also has passed from the first of three stages, the cumulus stage, into the second, or mature stage. An hour has elapsed and the storm will remain in the mature stage for another hour before changing into the final dissipating stage.

It is during the mature stage that our thunderstorm is most dangerous. A strong updraft, located in the middle and back sections

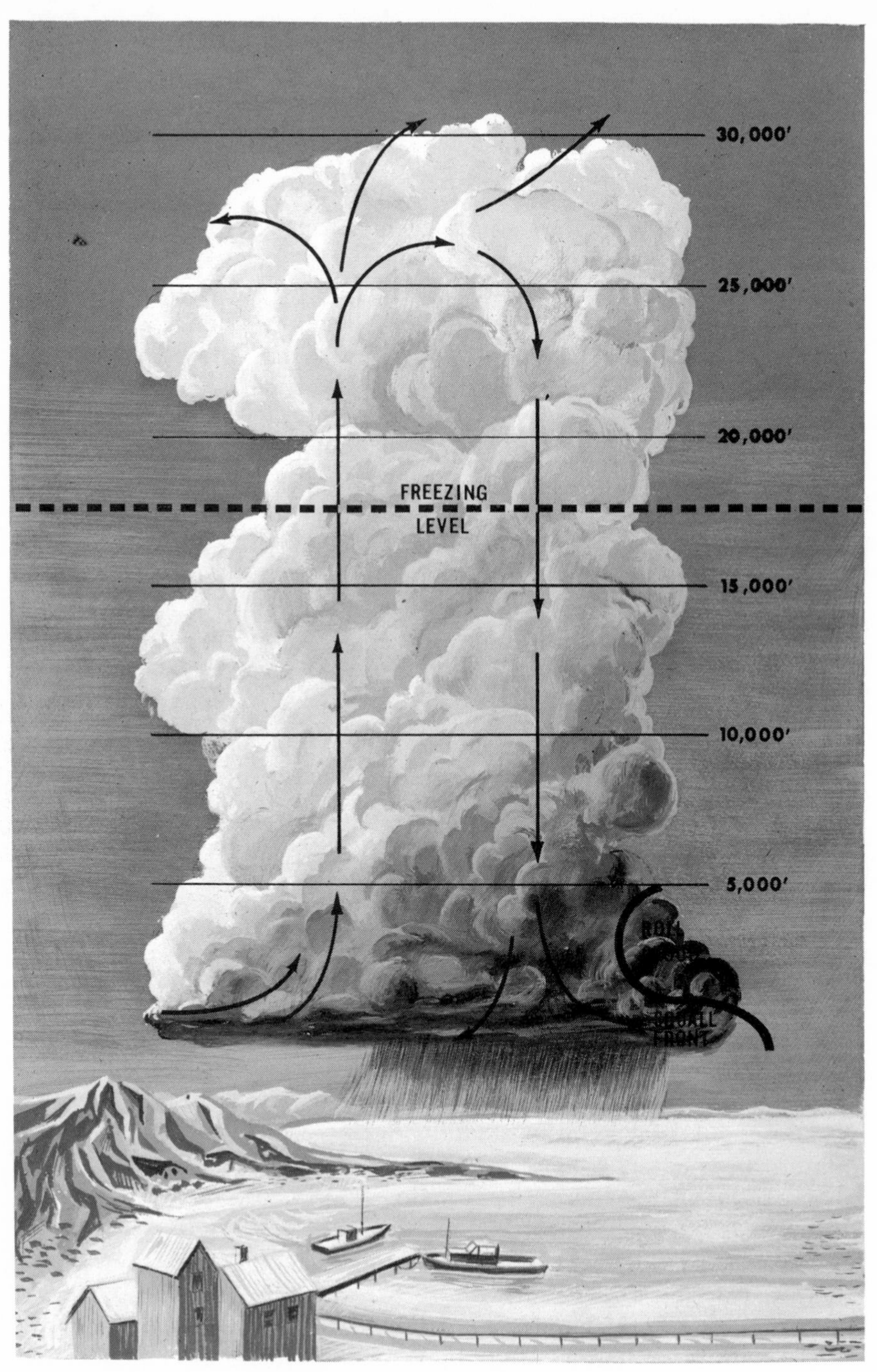

Fig. 14. A Typical Squall Cloud

of the cloud, feeds it with nourishing warm, moist air, and an equally vigorous downdraft hurls the spent, cold air downward from the top of the weather-factory cloud. Raindrops, carried aloft by the up-currents, freeze into hail and are either tossed out the side of the cloud or fall into the downdraft. Sometimes, the hailstones will bounce back and forth between the up- and down-currents, to pick up coatings of liquid water while below the freezing level, only to have them freeze into layers of ice as the stone is thrown back up into freezing air. In this manner, hailstones accumulate concentric layers and grow in size to as much as four inches. Normally, in coastal summertime thunderstorms the freezing level is high enough (over 15,000 feet) that the hail melts before reaching the ground.

As the thunderstorm draws near, we notice that it is growing not only in height, but in width as well, and is approximately four miles in diameter. The rain curtain is very dark, an opaque wall. And now we see something that sends a sinking feeling to the pit of the stomach. An ominous black roll cloud has formed on the leading edge of the storm. It is very low and deadly looking and we can clearly see its writhing turmoil as it scuds along over the water, revolving backwards.

The roll cloud is caused by an eddy effect between the forward edge of the cold downdraft and the warm, moist air flowing up from the surface. That is why it revolves backward (Figure 14). In spite of its fearsome appearance, the roll cloud is something of a fraud. It was once thought to be violent enough to rip an airplane apart, but recent studies of thunderstorms, in which aircraft flights were repeatedly made into this cloud, revealed that it is quite harmless.

The thunderstorm is now about a mile away and is as black as tar. Strangely enough—a bit ominously, we think—the wind and water around the boat are quiet. But spreading over the Bay, a half-mile ahead of the roll cloud, is the squall wind, the first gust of the thunderstorm. There is a sharp, clean-cut edge to the area of churning water and it is advancing upon us at a fast clip. Smooth water is suddenly beset with a confused rash of choppy, white-capped waves as the wind strikes it.

The helmsman swings the bow around to face the onrushing squall. And here it comes! A hard blast hits from the west . . . 25 . . . 30 . . . 40 knots. It is a chill, damp wind. The boat pitches sharply and we realize that, in a few short seconds, steep waves have formed. Stinging salt spray slaps our faces. The wind is pulsating. It drops briefly, but snaps right back up to come in hard, cold, 40

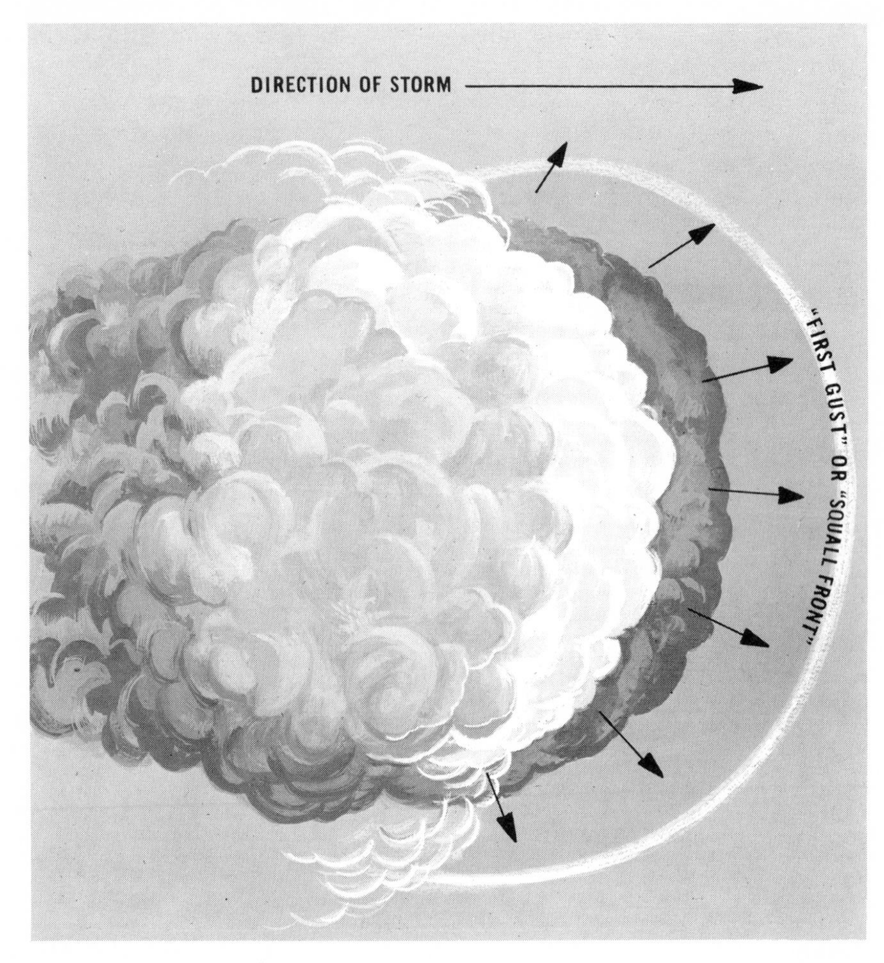

Fig. 15. Top View of a Squall Cloud

knot gusts. White cats' paws race frantically over the water's surface. Then the rain. Great drops beat a tattoo on the windshield, splatter against the sides. The rain is ice-cold. Visibility is cut to yards. The wind howls. It keeps up for five minutes, then begins to slacken. The raindrops are smaller now and visibility improves. Another ten minutes pass and the sky grows brighter, the wind is light, the water smooth once more. To the east, it is dark. The storm has passed on.

So that was a squall. Enough to make timid small-craft sailors remain at the yacht club permanently? No, because of several facts. Let us consider them.

In the first place, percentages are with the cautious sailor. Of all the thunderstorms that hover over boating areas, less than 10 percent have first-gust velocities that exceed 23 knots and a mere 3 percent contain squall winds greater than 30 knots. So, you see, our 40-knot squall was actually abnormal. These figures were lifted out of U. S. Weather Bureau Technical Paper *No.* 7, and are backed up by some of meteorology's best research efforts.

Another point to remember is that the effective time period of the first gust is limited. It is only during the mature stage of a thunderstorm's life that downdraft winds are strong enough to cause concern. This stage typically lasts about an hour. As long as the cloud has a rounded, hard-appearing top, it is still in the mature stage, but once the sheetlike anvil spreads out from its crown, we know that it has lost the updraft energy that built it and the dissipation stage has set in.

Precautions

The sailor's agility in dodging isolated squall clouds must not be underestimated. The typical squall we have just experienced could have been avoided by simply reversing course and heading south down Chesapeake Bay for a few miles. All you have to know is the course and speed of the thunderstorm cloud in order to steer clear of it. But how does one gather this information?

Well, there is always the seaman's weather eye, and no seaman should ever be without one. Watch the movement of the clouds. They drift at the whim of the wind currents, just as fallen leaves in a river are at the mercy of the water's flow. And, since the cumulonimbus squall cloud is only a cloud—though a rather monstrous one—it must advance with the pushing wind. However, the extreme height of the thunderstorm causes it to come under the influence of several layers of wind, so where is the steering level? It is somewhere in the middle, of course; from 10,000 to 20,000 feet, to be a little more exact. The wind direction and speed here can be obtained from the nearest U. S. Weather Bureau office when you call for the forecast before going a-cruising. If a weather station is not near, observe the movement of middle level clouds, the alto-cumulus and alto-stratus types. No middle clouds? Then low clouds will do, or just remember that most squalls will come out of a westerly (SW through NW) quadrant, because the upper winds are normally from that direction. The exception is when thunderstorms are imbedded in a tropical trade wind, which is an easterly flow in depth.

Not long ago, a boatman (who should have known better) was overheard to say, "There were several thunderheads along the coast, all moving in different directions. Two of them came together, and. . . ." Ain't so! They were all drifting in the same direction, with the wind, and in a straight-line path. Possibly two of them did join up to form a real spinaker-spanker, but, if so, they simply expanded sideways until they touched. That happens.

Some weatherwise skipper, no doubt, will pause here and muse, "But I recall a day last summer when the cumulus clouds were drifting with a south wind, and then there came roaring in from the northwest a big thunderstorm . . . a whole line of 'em, in fact." He will be right, but that "whole line of 'em" is the clue that a cold front was moving into the area and, with it, a shift in wind direction, both at the surface and aloft. The thunderstorms formed along the advance edge of the cold air mass because warm, light air was lifted bodily upward.

Cold Fronts and Squall Lines

Cold fronts are easily spotted on weather maps, though, and meteorologists can follow their progress from the time the fronts leave home in western Canada until they die in the arms of a tropical air mass off Florida. So, cold frontal thunderstorms should take no one by surprise.

Similar to cold fronts, and closely associated with them, are squall lines. These long lines of hefty thunderheads are normally oriented north-south and travel in an easterly direction. They run 100 or so miles in advance of fast moving cold fronts, and probably are caused by a pressure shock wave set off by the speeding cold front. Not all cold fronts have attendant squall lines—only the fast ones. Squall lines are found chiefly in the midwest, the states bordering the Gulf of Mexico, and the middle Atlantic coast. They are most active during spring and early summer. They, too, are predictable, and can be recognized while still far away. Watch for a line of cumulonimbus cloud tops in the west, or a general darkening of the western sky. A typical squall line advances at a speed of 25 knots, so the thunderstorms that can be seen nosing above the horizon will be on you in about an hour and a half.

Fig. 16-1. Top: First Stage in Development of a Squall Cloud
Fig. 16-2. Bottom: Second Stage in Development of a Squall Cloud

Stronger gusts come out of cold frontal and squall line thunderstorms than from the isolated variety, because they build higher and the resulting downdraft is brawnier. Just how strong do first gusts get? On July 3, 1948, the wind at Shreveport, La. reached 75 knots with passage of a squall line, and in June, 1953, Georgia's Lake Allatoona (2,000 boats on a good day) was churned by 65-knot gusts for a hectic ten minutes. Squalls of such velocities make news and are dutifully recorded in the press, but they are rare. A

Fig. 16-3. Third Stage in Development of a Squall Cloud

more realistic squall line wind would be around 40 knots. Even so, warnings will probably be flying when such a squall hoves into sight. The Severe Local Storm Forecasting Center, of the U. S. Weather Bureau at Kansas City, keeps a close watch on severe weather, nationwide, and flashes the warning to local weather stations for dissemination to the public.

Estimating Maximum Gusts

First gusts from isolated thunderstorms will normally be less. A good thumb rule in guessing at maximum gusts in an approaching storm is to add 15 knots to the estimated speed of movement of the cloud, or to the prevailing wind, if it is blowing from the direction of the storm's approach. If the cloud base is very low over the water, add another 10 knots. For example, let us assume a thunderstorm is moving in from the southwest. The prevailing wind is SW, 10 knots. That gives us an expected first-gust velocity of 25 knots. But, if the cloud base is low and gruesome looking, we would boost that expectancy to 35 knots. On the other hand, if the base is high (3,500 feet, or more) we would deduct 10 knots instead of adding, and the expected gust would be only 15 knots. The logic of the cloud-base-heights is that the downdraft wind is strongest at the base of the cloud and the closer we are to that base, the more wind. The downdraft of very high-based thunderstorms never reaches the ground. A typical thunderstorm bottom is near 1,000 feet.

Isolated thunderheads over the open ocean seldom contain strong surface gusts. The temperature contrast between sea and air is not great enough to generate husky updrafts; hence, no strong downdrafts. In fact, an ex-naval officer was heard to assert that seagoing thunderstorms have no gusts at all. Of course, most of them do, but he is prejudiced because of an experience during World War II.

He was Weather Officer on an escort carrier, a real clunker of a ship. Fresh out of the yard, with a clean hull, she could trample the waves at a breakneck 18 knots, but after a year in the tropical Pacific, that figure was reduced by a barnacled and rusty bottom. A good wind added to the ship's headway was required to launch heavy aircraft from her short deck. Daytime operations were easy enough, but the captain wanted to qualify his pilots in night landings. For the chosen night, the officer confidently forecast a bright moon and a brisk breeze.

At 2100, flight quarters was sounded and nervous aviators sat in their cockpits, with engines spluttering, waiting to fly off into the unknown. The moon was there, but where was that wind? For hours the carrier, followed by her brood of attendant destroyers, charged vainly over a glassy sea, searching for enough breeze to get the planes off. Big cumulo-nimbus clouds shone on all sides. The Weather Officer pointed them out to the skipper with the promise that under each there would be wind. But, as the ships steered from one cloud to another, all they found were flat calms and drenching tropical rains. Finally, the tired, wet, and frustrated hunters gave up and chugged into the anchorage at four o'clock in the morning. Later, the officer brought his weather map to the bridge and sheepishly tried to explain why no wind was to be had, but the Old Man barked at him to "get the hell below with that damned funny paper!"

Had the Captain listened, he would have learned from the "funny paper" that the big clouds stood stock-still because the upper, as well as the surface, winds were calm. This, plus the fact that high humidity of the sea air, enabling the thunderheads to build with a minimum of effort, made the clouds windless wonders.

But calm upper winds are not normal, and we small-craftsmen cannot hope to find many flat, calm "squall" clouds. We can learn to judge them coolly and try to avoid them, or beat to a lee shore. If that fails to work and it looks like a real boom-buster coming up, we can luff her and shorten sail, or heave to and drop a sea anchor. There is one good feature about squalls, as expressed by an old adage:

The sharper the blast,
The sooner she's past.

Chapter 6

Fog

The southeast wind had a wet, soggy feel about it. It was a gentle breeze and fairly warm, yet to the yachtsman cruising offshore, it smelled of weather. Not rough weather, like a sudden squall, but of fog. Although the sky was clear of clouds, the late afternoon sun low over the Atlantic coast 20 miles away shone with a weak yellow glow through the haze that covered the sea.

No sooner had the skipper wheeled his cruiser around to a heading for the channel entrance than in came the fog. Rolling over the ocean, the white bank moved with the wind. Silently it covered everything, a dripping, milky mass. Even the sea surface seemed subdued. Visibility was reduced to yards. But the boatman remained calm. The fog was no surprise to him. He had expected it and was ready with his exact position and just which course would take him safely in. He knew that in an hour he would pick up the outer whistle buoy, and from there he could follow the clangs of the bell buoys into the harbor.

Signs of Imminent Fog

An unprepared sailor might well have panicked at the abrupt change in the weather. But how did our yachtsman know that fog was imminent? First, there was the old and very practical (honorable, too) standby from the weatherman's bag of tricks, "historical sequence." Fog had been widespread along the coast the evening before, and the same air mass was present. Daytime heating had warmed the air enough to separate temperature and dew point and dissipate the fog. But with a little late-afternoon cooling, a repeat performance was almost certain.

The clear sky didn't fool him, either. The absence of clouds had no significance because clouds are the product of saturated air at higher altitudes, not necessarily of surface air, and the layer of air over the ocean was saturated. That was obvious, not only by the feel of it, but more specifically by the readings obtained by use of the sling psychrometer, a simple little gadget that tells much of fog possibilities. The look of the sky showed that the air was "loaded." Sea haze was present, robbing the sky of its deep blue color and reducing the powerful sun to an impotent yellow ball. Sea haze, composed of moisture and salt particles, furnishes excellent condensation nuclei for fog droplets to form on. Finally, the warm southeast wind blowing lightly over colder coastal water was the clincher. Our weatherwise seaman did not miss the implication there. That water was sure to cool the damp air by the few degrees needed for it to reach its dew point.

Here we have a classic example of conditions ripe for maritime, or sea, fog. One more factor might be added: time of year. From late fall to early summer, coastal waters are cold and more likely to trigger off the fog.

Sea fog is, perhaps, the most insidious kind. Its ornery character runs in the family, however, because it belongs to a particularly insidious group, the advection type. Advection fog may form at any time of day or night, and any time of year. It usually is widespread over large sections of the coast and open sea, and can last for days on end. It is caused when air is cooled to its dew point by being blown over a colder surface. The word advection denotes horizontal transport of air. The other main fog family, radiation, results from surface air being cooled to its dew point by the radiation of the earth's heat out into space during night-time cooling.

Note that, in each case, the key phrase is "air cooled to its dew point." That, indeed, is the crux of the whole fog discussion. Air temperature is a variable. The air becomes warm during an afternoon, only to cool off rapidly after dark. This daily variation in temperature often exceeds 25 degrees due to radiational cooling alone. On the other hand, dew point, which expresses the degree of moisture content of the air, remains constant. It changes very little from day to night because water vapor in the air mass is a tangible, real thing. The only way you can get rid of it within an air mass is to actually "rain" it out. Keep in mind that we are talking now about changes within the air that surrounds us. Of course, this air can be whisked away bodily, to be replaced by a mass with entirely different characteristics. Recall, from Chapter 2, that air masses of conflicting personalities are separated by fronts, and that these fronts move across the weather map in a predictable pattern.

Fig. 17. Sea Fog Can Come in During Day or Night

So, sudden variations in humidity should not be expected to confuse the issue. Moisture can be added through evaporation from a water surface, but this is a slow, gradual process usually requiring several days to change the dew point noticeably.

Moisture in the atmosphere is the cause of weather and, since it it so important, several ways of measuring and describing it are used. Among these are: absolute humidity, specific humidity, mixing ratio, vapor pressure, and wet bulb temperature. The first

Fig. 18. Sea Fog is Formed by Warm Damp Air Invading Colder Coastal Waters

three express water vapor by weight, and are useful for scientific studies, but of little use to the do-it-yourself weatherman. Vapor pressure is impractical to use, and wet bulb temperature, while useful for some things, does not serve the purpose of weather forecasting quite as well as dew point. Dew point is a temperature and is easily compared to air temperature when thinking of the chances for fog.

Relative humidity is descriptive and certainly is widely used and understood by most people. To say that the air is "50-percent saturated" conveys an immediate impression. The trouble is, it is too relative. The percentage of humidity can, and does, vary radically with changes in temperature, even though the actual amount of water vapor present remains the same. Relative humidity can be 40 or 50 percent at noon and, by midnight, 100 percent, due to nothing more than a change in temperature.

What about dew point? It is that temperature at which saturation (100 percent relative humidity) will occur. Suppose we have a midday air temperature of 70 degrees with a 60-degree dew point. As the sun goes down and the earth begins to cool, the air cools, too. By 10:00 P.M., say, the temperature has fallen to 65 degrees, and at 2:00 A.M. it is 60 degrees. The dew point is also 60 degrees. Remember, it does not change. Now the air is saturated. Any further lowering of temperature will result in an excess of water vapor in the air, which must be "wrung out." This is done by the deposit of dew (hence the term "dew point") on the ground, provided the air is motionless. If a bit of a breeze is stirring, this moisture will form as visible fog droplets suspended in the air.

Fog droplets are very small and light. They float in the air just as do cloud particles. In fact, fog is simply a cloud on the surface. But why doesn't rain fall from fog as it does from clouds? It does, on occasion. Once fog has formed, the cooling process of air is slowed greatly and the temperature remains close to that point. Additional cooling is hampered by the release of the latent heat of condensation, which is generated during the change of water vapor into visible form. However, now and then, saturated air continues to cool despite this generated heat. As the temperature goes down, so must the dew point, and the wrung-out moisture falls as a slow drizzle to create a "dripping fog." Rain heavier than this fine drizzle does not fall from fog because a great depth of cloud is needed for the large drops. In a deep cloud layer, the small droplets grow in size gradually as they fall through the saturated air, picking up more and more water.

Fog is one weather element that can be affected by the works of man. Fog incidence has been raised near industrial centers by pollution of the air with chemical smoke. Certain particles, such as the sulfides, attract water droplets and encourage fog formation. London's Black Fogs are that way because of the concentrated soft coal smoke hanging over the city under stable atmospheric conditions.

(Official U.S. Navy Photo.)

Fig. 19. Arctic Sea Fog is More of a Curiosity Than a Hazard

Fog Classifications

Most fogs cannot be said to belong completely to one classification, but are usually a combination of two or more types. The sea fog that moved in so rapidly at the beginning of this chapter was of the advection family; nevertheless, it was triggered off by late-afternoon radiational cooling. Even early morning ground fog that hangs in meadows and near creek beds—considered to be a purely radiational type—is frequently accentuated by cool air draining down into the lowlands from nearby high ground, and thereby acquires an advection flavor.

Radiation Fog

Pure radiation fog is of no great concern to sailors because it is a phenomenon of the land. Only land cools rapidly at night, thus enabling ground fog to form. Water gives up its heat much more slowly and does not change (more than a degree or two) from the heat of the day to the cool of the night. Therefore, true "ground" fog does not exist at sea. It can drift over small lakes and land-locked harbors of the coast, but normally thins out when warmed by the water.

Since it is difficult to find a fog that has not been assisted in its formation or intensification by the radiation process, it might be well to look at the criteria that must be met for radiation fog. First, there must be enough moisture in the air mass. The dew point must be high enough so that the air temperature could conceivably reach it when cooled. Then, there must be a clear sky to enable the heat radiated out of the earth to escape into space. Even a high, thin cloud layer will slow the cooling remarkably. The wind must be light (2–6 knots), but not calm. If the air is still, only dew will form, but if the wind blows too strong, the air layers near the ground will be disturbed and the cool surface air will be dispersed.

The mechanics of condensation are the same for all types of fog. It is the manner in which the air is cooled that determines fog classification. As members of the two main families already mentioned, there are cold-front, warm-front, precipitation, river, ground, steam fogs, and, of course, sea fog. Some meteorologists have assigned additional, even more exotic, names but these pretty well cover the field. Let us look at them more closely.

Weather associated with fronts ranges from the worst to the best, depending on a number of "ifs", such as location, time of year, temperatures, and humidities of the air masses involved, speed of movement, and others. So we cannot generalize too much about fronts and their attendant weather. This is especially true regarding frontal fog because a minority of fronts contain fog. But, if we consider only those weather fronts of interest to sailors—that is, the ones in a maritime setting—then the likelihood of fog is increased. Eliminate summer fronts, and the fog-index is raised once more. Slow the frontal movement to a walk, step up the moisture content of the air near the front, and now we are talking fog.

Fog in a slowly moving cold front is due to the mixing of warm, moist air with colder air. Air temperature is lowered to the dew point by this mixing, and the inevitable happens. Night-time cooling aids the fog process and so frontal fog is usually most dense at night and in early morning.

Fig. 20. River Fog is Often Seen to Travel in Well-defined Clouds

Precipitation Fog

Fog is more at home in and around warm fronts because, in such cases, tropical air is brought bodily into colder regions, allowing contact cooling of the warm air by colder ground or sea. Warm frontal fog and precipitation fog go hand in hand. They are like close companions; you seldom find one without the other.

Precipitation fog results when surface air is loaded with water vapor by rain falling steadily through it. This commonly happens in warm fronts. This type defies placement in either the advection or radiation families, but leans more to the advection class. Precipitation fog is of more interest to aviators than seamen because visibility usually is not reduced to less than a half-mile. Even with veteran weather observers, it is a moot question whether visibility in this fog type is cut down more by the falling rain or by true fog particles. Not that it matters. But if the rain stops suddenly, how much of the fog will remain?

Precipitation fog is not found with showers or thunderstorms. It slips into an area only with steady, prolonged winterlike rains. Temperature and dew point separation at the onset of the rain might be misleading. Frequently, rain falls into very dry surface air and, at first, visibility is unlimited. But evaporating raindrops soon load the air with moisture and saturation results in a short time.

River Fog

River fog is somewhat of a paradox in that it is set off by advection of water into a region of warmer air. Cold water flowing downstream from high ground or a northern origin cools surface air by contact. Often, river fog is seen to travel downstream in well-defined "clouds," indicating surges of colder water. Not only is river fog a hazard to river boatmen, but frequently to craft operating in harbors and coastal sections near the mouths of cold rivers, where the fresh water retains its identity and fog-making capabilities.

River fog is also subject to the whims of man's toying with natural resources. River temperatures in many localities have been changed by the construction of dams. Georgia's Chattahoochee River, for example, was once reasonably free of fog. But after the erection of Buford Dam, upstream from Atlanta, the river water is colder by ten degrees because it is released through the dam from the bottom of a deep lake. Dense river fog is now almost a daily affair on warm, humid days.

Steam Fog

Steam fog, or "Arctic Sea Smoke," is more of a curiosity than a problem. An extremely cold air mass settling over warm water will speed up evaporation of the water body, and the moisture released rises vertically in miniature convective currents. Rapid cooling soon condenses the vapor into visible form. Fog streamers thus formed normally taper off at a height of six feet or so, but some have been observed to rise several hundred feet. Steam fog is annoying, but boat operators seldom have trouble picking their way through the columns of mist.

Sea Fog

Sea fog has been called "the only true advectional fog." Even so, night-time radiational cooling and daytime warming have their effects, especially near the coast. Out where sea fog is at home, these day-night influences are negligible.

Fig. 21. River Fog Spilling Over the Banks of The Broad River in South Carolina

Where is the habitat of sea fog? Simply, it is wherever cold and warm water currents are in close proximity. The sea area around Newfoundland is a prime example. The cold Labrador current flowing down from the northwest practically collides with the balmy Gulf Stream sweeping grandly up from the U. S. east coast. Of course, it is not the mixture of these waters that causes trouble, but the fact that air moving over the warm water has acquired warm, wet characteristics, and when this air meets the cold Labrador current, it is cooled radically. Widespread and dense fog is the result. The same thing happens in the area of the Aleutian Islands, as well as a dozen or more other such places around the oceans.

To cite cases nearer home, the famous "Golden Gate fog" of California is generated when warm winds blowing in from the Pacific pass over cold sea water near the coast. Gulf Coast fog is a natural at times when the shallow inshore waters have been chilled by winter rains or a series of cold-air invasions. Breezes from far out in the tropical Gulf soon become fog-ridden as they sweep in over this cold water.

The Psychrometer

In almost every discussion of fog, use of the sling psychrometer pops up. This is to be expected, because the psychrometer tells us the humidity of the air. By taking frequent readings, we can watch changes in the air's moisture content and judge whether or not fog is likely. But the usual mistake is to oversimplify fog and its forecasting, and to portray the psychrometer as a never-fail, foolproof forecasting tool.

Usually included in psychrometer instructions is a table or graph to show time of fog formation based on the rate of change in temperature and dew point spread. If, for example, the spread between these two temperatures is ten degrees in the midafternoon and it closes to six degrees by sunset, then the assumption is made that this difference will continue to decrease at a steady rate and that fog will result when the temperature and dew point are the same. In this simplified case, fog would be forecast to form shortly after midnight.

Forecasting fog just is not that easy. If it were, then we could expect to have fog 365 days a year in many places, because it is normal for air temperature to begin dropping after the heat of the afternoon has passed. But that does not mean that air will continue to cool right on down to the dew point every night. The cooling usually stops at a point a few degrees shy of saturation. Consider the fact that, even on the New England Coast, there are only 60 days or so a year with dense fog.

This is not to belittle the use of the psychrometer. Indeed, meteorologists watch temperature-dew point relationships very closely. Figure 22 is a simple graph to project the narrowing difference between air temperature and dew point to the fog-point.

Starting at zero hours on the horizontal scale, plot two points to depict the spread between temperature and dew point. The dew point reading is always placed at O on the vertical scale. The temperature mark is then made to show the difference in degrees F. In our example, the initial spread is 10 degrees. Actual temperature is not important—it is the spread that matters. Plot hourly readings on the graph and watch the changes. Dew point will usually remain constant, or climb slowly. Project the trend forward to the meeting of the two lines, indicating saturation. In Figure 22, that occurs 12 hours after the first observation was made.

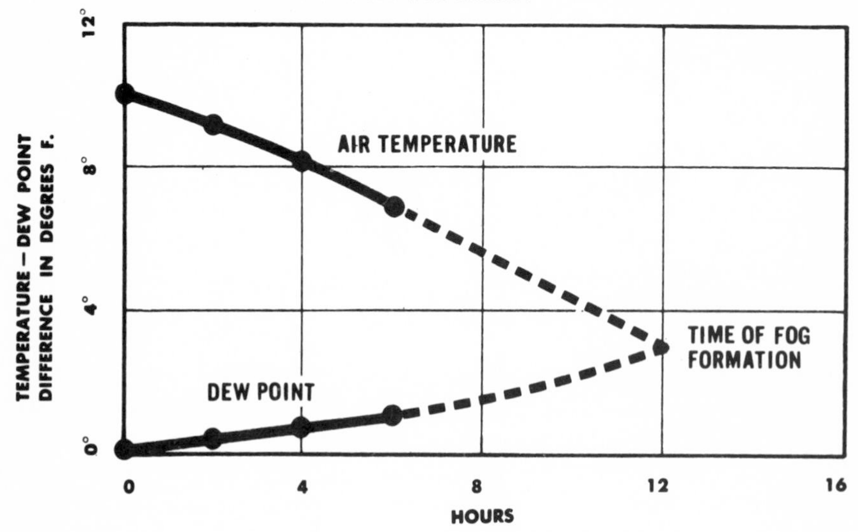

Fig. 22. Fog Forecasting Graph

Check-off List for Fog Forecasting

Use this chart, but remember that fog requires that "little extra something." Here is a simple check-off list for fog forecasting.

Historical sequence. Did fog form in this area last night? Are weather conditions about the same?

Wind. Is it blowing warm, damp, and steady with no gustiness? Not too strong, and noticeably warmer than the water?

Temperature–Dew point. Are they within ten degrees of each other? Is the expected minimum temperature close to the present dew point?

Sky and air. Does the sky appear hazy and not very blue? Horizon ill-defined? At night, do light beams from spotlights or lighthouses appear "misty?"

Is the time of year right?

If "yes" is the answer to these questions, then stand by.

Once fog has formed, the next problem is, when will it break? Again, historical sequence should be considered. When did it lift yesterday? That may seem like an idiotic approach, but take it from a meteorologist, the professionals check that one on their lists first.

Warming of the lower layer of air by the sun takes credit for the "burning off" of fog in most cases. Except in the heart of winter in

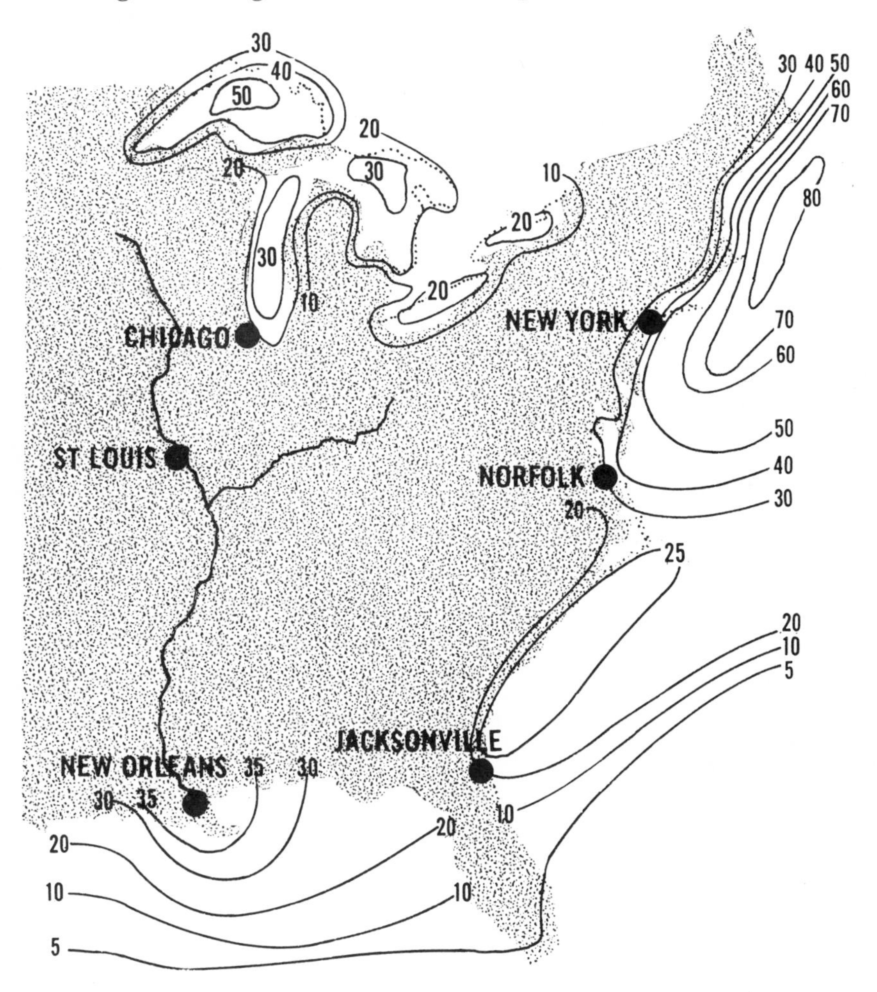

Fig. 23. Number of Days Per Year With Dense Fog

higher latitudes, the sun sends enough heat down to penetrate even thick fog. The warm-up will be slow, especially if the wind is moderate, but if your thermometer shows a steady climb, then fog dissipation is just a matter of time. If rain is falling through the fog, expect no sun heating.

A change in wind direction will often "blow away" the fog. Such a shift would mean the transport in of a different mass of air, one that might be drier. An increase in wind usually lifts the fog off the surface, forms a low cloud deck, and succeeds in improving surface visibility. So, if you are fog-bound, whistle for a strong wind, particularly an offshore one.

It is difficult to check the latest weather map when you are anchored two miles out in pea soup, but often the riddle of "when" can be solved by a glance at the big picture. Maybe a cold front, bringing in cold, dry air, is just around the corner. Take the trouble to look at the weather map before cruising, even if it is only that one found in the newspaper or on TV. Listen to one word of caution before jumping to a conclusion that fog is imminent, despite the fact that many signs may point to fog. Most cruising areas get little dense fog. Check the fog frequency chart, Figure 23, and note the relatively small number of fog days on most coasts. Exercise caution even in the use of such charts, because many of these are prepared for and by aviation interests. To an aviator, any ceiling less than 500 feet is classed as fog. We boatmen have enough problems without going several hundred feet in the air to find fog.

Chapter 7

Sailor's Wind

Wind is air in motion.

Almost every discussion of wind begins with that time-honored cliché, so we may as well say it and be done with it. The person who coined the phrase no doubt meant to deflate wind from an overbearing bully to an understandable weather element. That is good, because wind has always been a bit mysterious to the sailor. To the iron men (of wooden-ship fame) who depended upon it for power, and who were at its whim, wind especially seemed to be an animate, living thing.

To the Ancient Mariner, "He was tyrannous and strong, and struck with his o'erpowering wings and chased us south along." To Masefield, it cut "like a whetted knife" and "blew like the Bull of Barney, a beast of a breeze."

Wind is Weather at Sea

On the water, wind *is* weather. Of course, fog and rain are important, but it is wind that stirs up the sea, makes the sailor take in canvas, and makes him head in to the harbor. To be impressed with the fact that wind is simply air in motion is a big step in understanding what it is all about.

Weather-Map Winds

Air is set in motion to compensate for differences in barometric pressure over different areas. Wind is a bodily transport of air from higher to lower pressure. On a grand scale, the winds of the general circulation span the globe to balance out the pressure differential caused by unequal heating of the equatorial and polar regions. In the secondary circulation, winds blow from dense *highs* to fill *lows*. These are weather-map winds. They flow across isobars at an angle of about 15 degrees. The more closely spaced the isobars, the faster the winds, because isobars on a weather map show atmospheric pressure contours just as contours on a topographical map show ground height. A ball would roll faster down the slope of a steep hill, one with closely-spaced contours, than a gentle one. So it is with air flowing down atmospheric "hills."

On a smaller scale, air flows through valleys, from cool sea to warm land, "katabatically" down hills, and around and around the low pressure vortices of backyard dust devils. It is in the world of "local" winds that we will delve mainly, because the man in the sailboat is propelled by local winds, not by the general circulation. But local winds cannot be divorced entirely from the secondary circulation because the two are intertwined, superimposed on each other. So, it is always wise to size up the gradient wind (the weather-map wind) before fooling around with locally-influenced breezes.

The Sea Breeze

A classic local wind is the familiar sea breeze. The sea breeze has been studied intensely by meteorologists because it represents the most fundamental of atmospheric processes. It is a small-scale monsoon wind. In fact, a miniature of the global general circulation.

The sea breeze is caused by the temperature difference between coastal land and water areas. Water temperature changes very slowly. There is practically no daily variation. On the other hand, land temperature has a wide daily range—about 20 degrees in summer. This sets up a situation wherein a radical temperature contrast may exist in a distance of a few miles. Let us take a case.

It is a morning in August. Along the coast of Rhode Island, the sky is a clear blue and visibility is excellent. It should be, because a cold front passed through the day before. The cool dome of a *high* is centered over the Great Lakes, with a gradient wind over Rhode Island of northwest at 6 knots. The temperature at Providence is 68 degrees. The sea water temperature offshore, near Block Island, is 70 degrees. As the sun climbs higher, the land warms, and so does the air layer immediately over it. By midmorning, the temperature along the Rhode Island beaches, and inland, is 76 degrees. This warming has caused the air to expand and become lighter. It begins to rise in weak updrafts. Pressure is reduced. But remember that the temperature of the water has not changed, nor has that of the air above it, so the air pressure offshore remains constant. This denser air wants to flow inland to the lower pressure over land, but the gradient wind is bucking it.

A "push-o'-war" ensues and the wind slackens along the coast to a near standstill while the two forces press against each other. The direction backs around to west as a compromise. By noon, the land has warmed to 81 degrees, and the sea breeze can be held off no longer, so in it comes. It is still weak, but as the inland temperatures continue to rise, the onshore wind is stronger. It settles on a direction of SW, because the gradient wind is still in there fighting, even though outclassed. Had there been no gradient wind—a flat calm prevailing—the sea breeze would have come in earlier and stronger, and would have assumed a direction at a right angle to the coastline.

In Florida, for example, a typical summer afternoon will find sea breezes blowing into the peninsular from nearly every direction (except north), depending on how the coast lies.

If the gradient wind is already coming in from the sea, then the sea breeze velocity is added to it. The prevailing direction in the New York area is south during the summer months, due to the return flow from the far edge of the Bermuda *high.* Add to this the daily southerly sea breeze and it is easy to see why Long Island Sound, and the entire section, enjoys top-notch sailing conditions.

The sea breeze reaches its high point during midafternoon, the time of greatest contrast between land and water temperatures. It then slackens in proportion to the cooling of the land, finally dying out when land and sea temperatures are the same. As the land continues to cool by radiation, a land breeze sets in. This offshore reciprocal of the sea breeze is weak and generally ineffectual.

Since the force of the sea breeze is in direct proportion to the temperature contrast between land and water, there are small fluctuations in the wind speed along shores. The onshore wind will be more brisk blowing into a hot city or open fields than into a forest or inland lake section.

Convection, vertical upcurrents of hot air, is the mechanism that sets off the sea breeze and sustains it. Convection is also the mother of cumulus showers and thunderstorms, so we would expect to find cumulus activity over land when the sea breeze is blowing. If there is sufficient moisture in the air, thunderstorms do build. If there is a lesser amount of water vapor, showerless cumulus will form. But we must not assume that just because the wind is coming in over the water, it is moist. The air might be damp in the lower hundred feet or so, but dry above.

In fact, in cases like the Rhode Island sea breeze, cited above, it is likely that the onshore wind is dry because, after all, it was a northwest wind that merely went to sea for a few miles, then turned around and came back. Inland showers and thunderstorms are quite prevalent with a sea breeze that has had a long maritime history.

Showers and thunderstorms induced by onshore winds hang back a few miles inland as long as the wind blows. In the late afternoon or evening, these storms often drift out over the sea. At times, the upper level winds force them seaward despite the sea breeze. Frequently, the edge of the cumulus cloud mass is poised just above the shoreline, where the sea breeze is first lifted by the hot land. The curve of the coast is plainly discernable by following these clouds.

It is an aviator's trick to fly down the Florida coast in summer, just offshore, remaining under a clear sky. A few miles away, inside the shoreline, an almost solid mass of thunderstorms often flails the hapless pilot who chooses the inland route.

The pure sea breeze is small in scope. It rarely extends more than 15 miles to seaward, or 15 miles inland. Notice the word "pure." If the sea breeze is an accentuation of a larger gradient flow—as is normally the case with the southwest sea breeze around New York—then these figures do not hold. It is a shallow wind with a depth of less than 2000 feet. That explains why clouds, even low clouds, often move against the sea breeze. Its velocity is about 10 knots and rarely exceeds 20 knots. It is a stable wind, with little gustiness and not much deviation in direction.

Atmospheric Stability

Mention of a stable wind brings up the subject of atmospheric stability again. It was discussed in Chapter 2, but since this has such an important bearing on the character of surface wind, we shall discuss it briefly here.

Whether air is stable or unstable depends on the vertical temperature distribution aloft. It is normal for temperature to decrease with altitude at a rate of about 3 degrees per thousand feet. If it cools upward more rapidly than this rate, the air is unstable. If the temperature increases aloft, as it often does for short stretches, the air is stable. In other words, warm air over cold is a stable condition. Cold air over warm is unstable. The reason, of course, is that cold air is heavier and tends to sink. If it is on top, a tumbling, or overturning, takes place. However, if the lower layer is cold, with warm air above, only stable horizontal currents result.

What does stability have to do with wind? To begin with, upper winds are stronger than surface winds, because air moving over the ground is slowed down by surface friction. In fact, we must go up to 2000 feet to overcome this drag effect. Now, with a stable condition in the upper air, the frictionless winds above slide easily over the cooler surface blanket of air, leaving it undisturbed. This gives a steady, non-gusty wind. But when the air is unstable, updrafts and downdrafts are rife throughout the atmosphere. It is the strong downdrafts that strike the surface and make gusts. In short, surface wind gusts are simply reflections of "batches" of the upper level winds that have plunged to earth. Gustiness is greater during daytime than at night because normal nighttime cooling gives the ground a protective layer of cool air, allowing the gradient wind to slide over the top.

If the surface wind and upper winds are from the same direction, then surface wind gustiness will be exhibited chiefly in velocity. But if the upper winds are blowing counter to surface winds, then the wind direction will suffer wide deviation in the gusts. This is shown clearly in Figure 29. Compare the extreme wind directional change of a pre-hurricane squall with that of a typical summer thunderstorm. Incidentally, meteorologists predict maximum possible gusts from the speed of winds aloft at levels up to 5000 feet. Surface gusts cannot exceed this speed.

In Figures 24–29, characteristic wind traces are shown for different air masses and wind types. Northwest winds, hauling in *cPk* air, are gusty because *k* air is colder than the surface (remember?) and is unstable. Strong downdrafts dive to the ground, causing wild fluctuations in wind speed and direction. A northeast wind, usually associated with *mPk* air, is not quite as radical. Even though it is a *k* type, it is not as cold and unstable as *cPK*.

The sea breeze, assigned a direction of southeast in this case, is a stable wind. The convective activity that produced it makes it vary somewhat in direction and velocity as it nears the shore.

The southwest wind, composed of *mTw* air, is the smoothest of all. Stratified air layers above do not mix and gustiness is nil. Folks out in the tornado belt dislike southwest winds. They speak of the "steady pressure" of the wind, the unrelenting flow, and tell of how tree leaves stand out, unmoving, just before a twister strikes. It is an anachronism that the epitome of instability, the tornado, should begin in such stable air. However, there are extenuating circumstances. The *mTw* air furnishes warmth and our old friend, Copious Water Vapor, but in order to have a tornado there must be a high (above 10,000 feet), cold, and very dry current above the southwest wind. Then there must be a hefty triggering mechanism, such as a squall line or cold front, to boost the warm air up through the cold, dry layer. These three factors must get together with perfect timing. Since this seldom happens, tornadoes are really quite rare, despite the big splash they get in the newspapers when they do occur.

The southwest wind, then, is stable only if it is pulling in a solid mass of *mTw* air. If there is an overrunning cold flow at high levels, it may be extremely gusty.

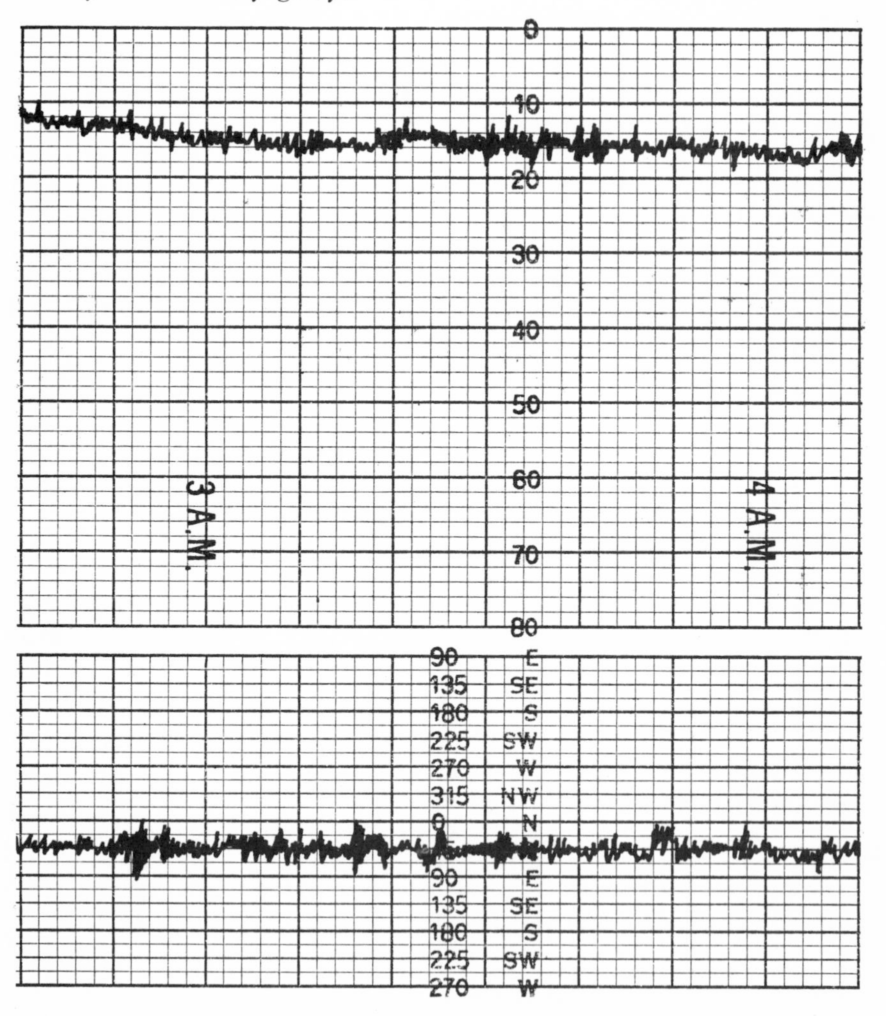

Fig. 24. Wind Trace of Northeast Wind

Bear in mind that the wind traces in Figures 24–29 were recorded at a land station. Wind over the sea is always a bit less gusty, but stronger.

How does the boatman tell whether the air is stable or unstable? Well, he can ask the local Weather Bureau office before cruising. But if he is already aboard, he can tell a lot by just looking around. Low clouds are good indicators. Are they stratified (stable), or cumuloform (unstable)? If the sky is clear, then how about visi-

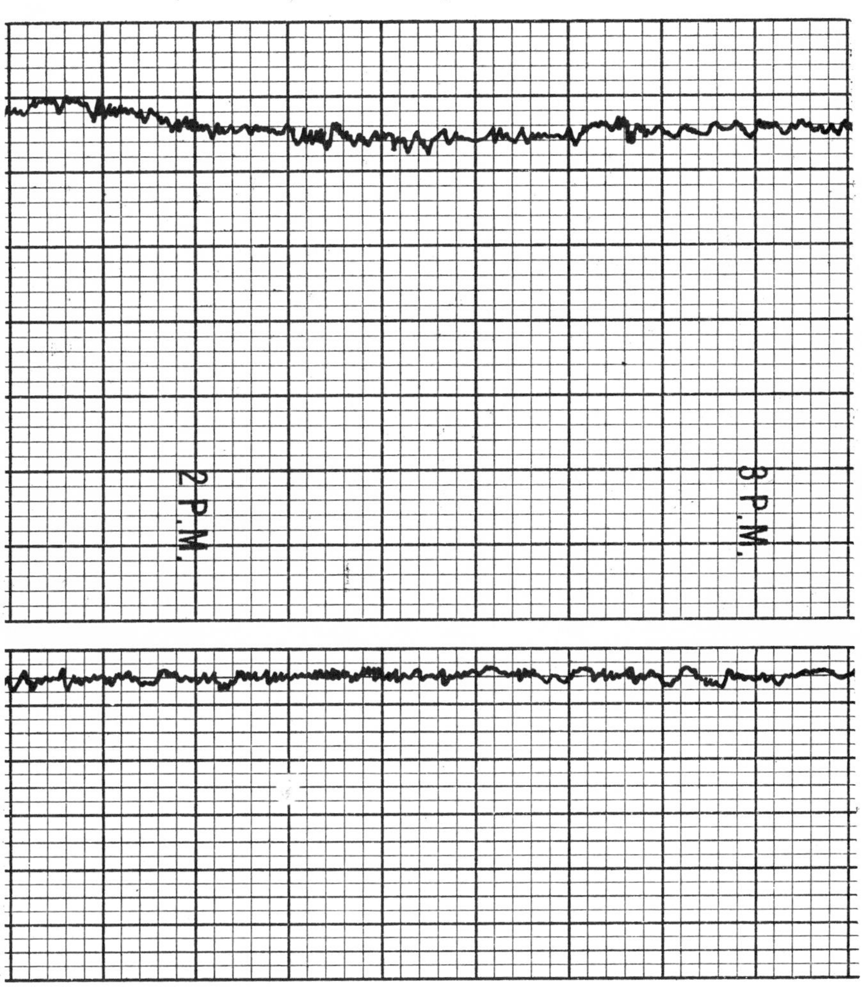

Fig. 25. Wind Trace of Southeast Wind

bility? Is the day hazy (stable), or is the horizon clearly defined (unstable)? Does smoke hang low, or in stratified layers in the air (stable), or is the sky a bright blue (unstable)? Is water temperature much cooler than the air (stable), or warmer (unstable)?

If low clouds are moving rapidly in the morning, there are strong winds aloft that will cause fresh and gusty surface winds once the temperature inversion has been broken by sun heating. But if the low clouds are creeping along, then so is the gradient wind.

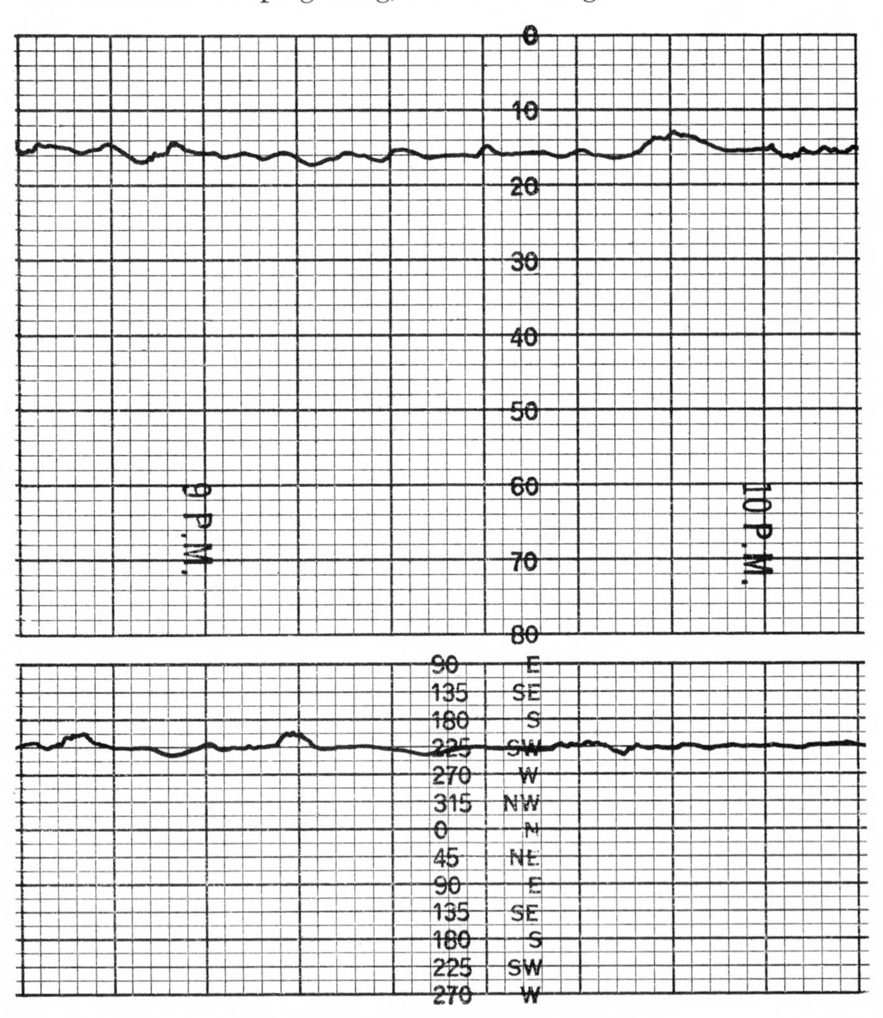

Fig. 26. Wind Trace of Southwest Wind

There are a few more points to consider before leaving atmospheric stability. Unstable winds, especially if they are cold, are "heavier" against the sail than warm, smooth winds. They actually exert more force. And it has been found by British meteorologists that wind waves on the water will be steeper and more troublesome when the wind is unstable and gusty.

The study of wind has especially interested European weathermen. The British relentlessly track the movements of aphids and

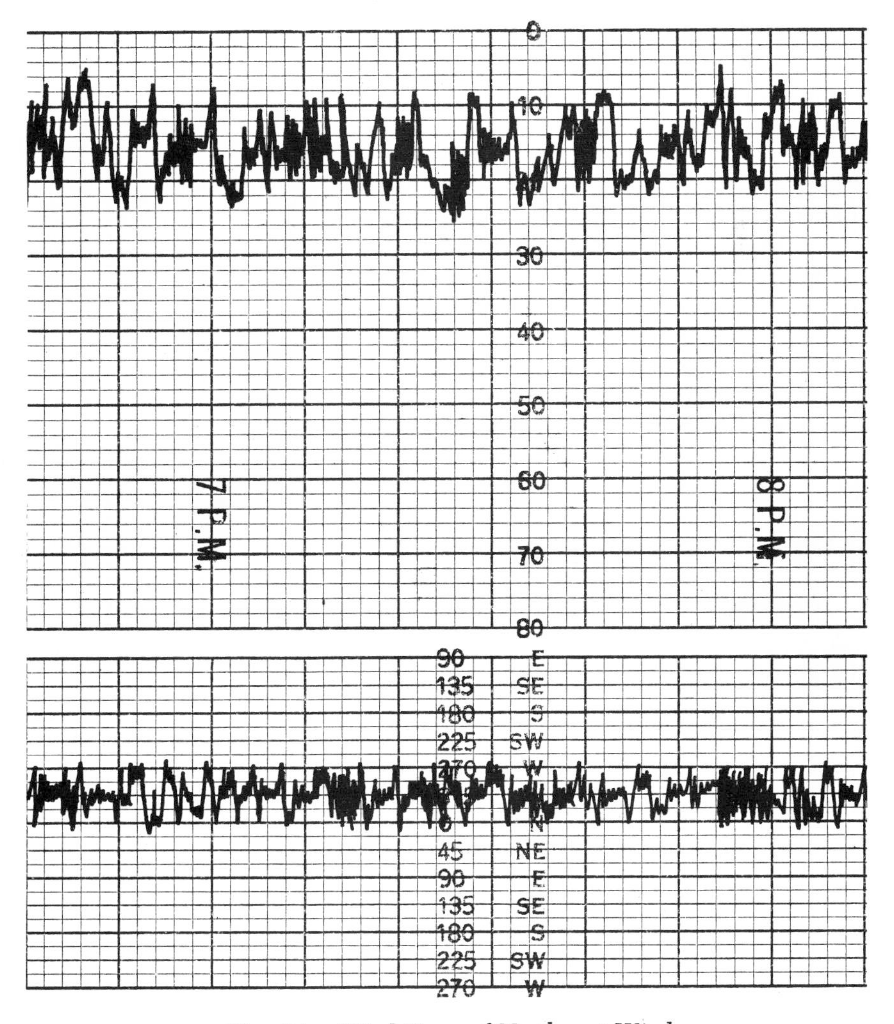

Fig. 27. Wind Trace of Northwest Wind

locusts (in Africa) to determine wind currents, and one of the world's most authoritative books on micrometeorology was written by a German who spent years investigating wind over the ground. He found that air flows most easily over snow cover, then over a close-cropped grass lawn, high grass, a turnip field, and a wheat field. Inland waters rank with the grass lawn.

A typical wind blowing over the water will increase, say, from 3 knots on the surface to 4 knots 7 feet up, and to 5 knots at 15 feet.

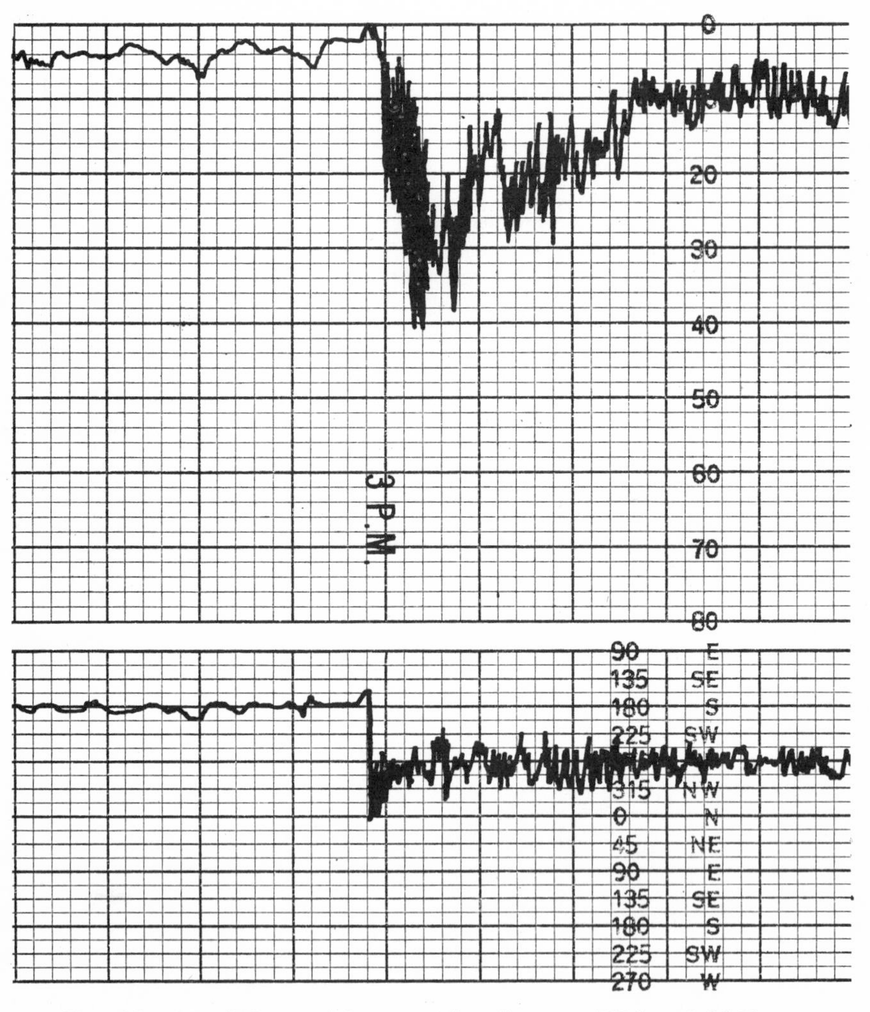

Fig. 28. Wind Trace of Summer Thunderstorm With a Cold Front

This increase continues logarithmically up to the top of the "friction" layer at 2000 feet. Over the open ocean, the wind at 33 feet is conceded to be two-thirds the frictionless wind speed. Over land, the 33-foot wind is one-third the velocity of the unaffected wind. Wind direction can also change within a short distance above the surface. Square-rigged ships were seen, now and then, with skysails and royals set at an angle different from staysails and lower-topsails to take advantage of shearing winds.

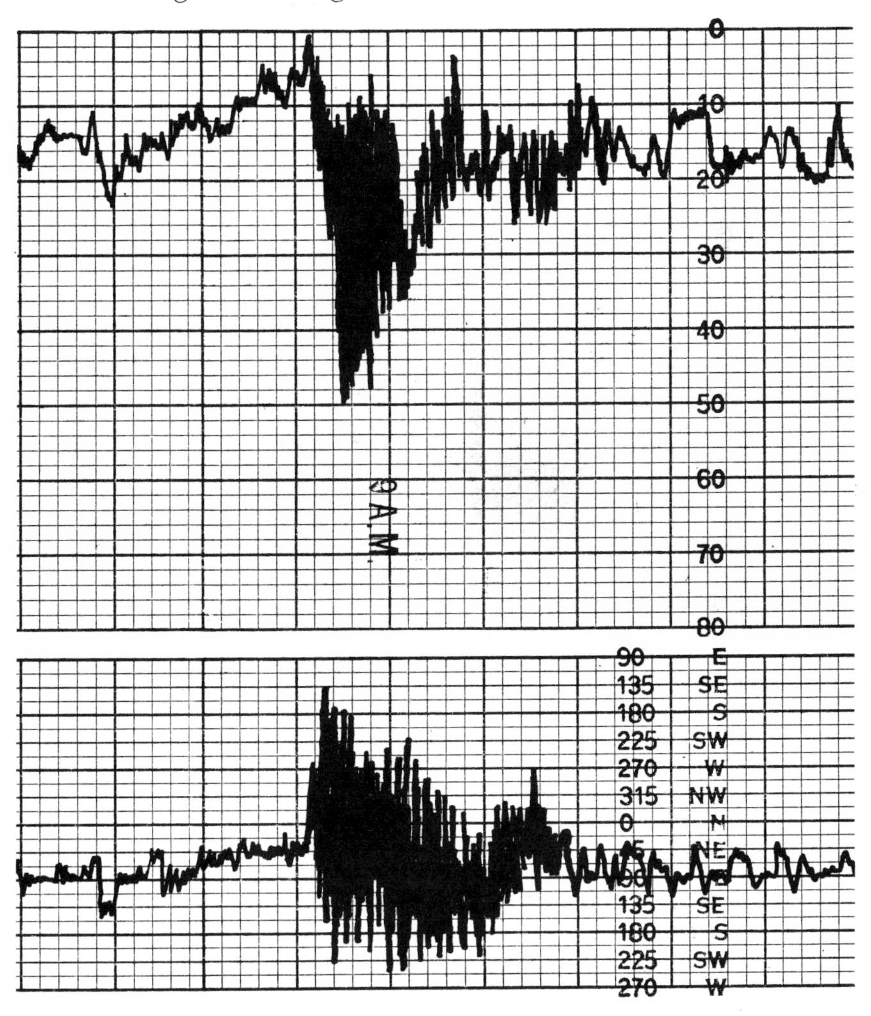

Fig. 29. Wind Trace of Pre-hurricane Squall

Surface obstacles do, indeed, slow the wind. The author recently sailed in a sound where the wind was 10 knots over the water, peaking up occasional white caps. Wind at sail-top was estimated at 15 knots. Along the sound's edge was a large area of marsh grass, 3 feet high. The water was smooth for 90 feet to leeward of the grass. Cutting through the marsh was a narrow channel, no wider than the boat. It was quite a sensation to speed close-hauled through the glassy water, propelled by a fresh masthead breeze.

Fig. 30. Line of Thunderstorms Over Land Fed by Onshore Sea Breeze

Effective windbreaks, such as a thickly foliaged tree-stand, reduce surface wind for a distance to windward that is seven times the height of the obstacle, and a distance of thirty times the obstacle's height to leeward. That is not to say the wind is completely blocked, but is merely reduced in speed. It is also made more turbulent and shifty. The dead-air space is one and one half times the height to windward, and four times the height to leeward. If the obstacle is somewhat streamlined and isolated, then these figures will be modified downward. An example would be a rounded island in a lake or along a rocky coast. Air will flow around, as well as over, such an island.

If the slope of an obstacle is less than 45 degrees, the wind will be relatively unaffected, but if greater than 45 degrees, maximum blocking will be felt.

On the lee shore of an island, the wind will come in around the sides at right angles to the unaffected flow, and over the top of the island to form a reverse eddy blowing into the lee shore. The stronger the wind, the larger the dead-air space will be. Wind will follow steep shorelines (with tall trees or high ground borders) and channels between land areas unless the wind is a sea breeze. Sea breezes tend to blow into the shore, because it is the "pull" of the land that induces them. A good rule to remember regarding sea breezes is that the hotter the land, the stronger the pull on a sea breeze.

An onshore wind will be deviated by a steep headland, such as a cliff, and "split." This includes sea breezes, if the headland is not barren and hot. A cove or flat beach bordered by two steep headlands will have the wind funneled into it. The velocity of this converging wind will be stronger than normal. Closely-grouped sailboats can have somewhat the same effect as a headland.

Apparent Wind vs. True Wind

The matter of apparent wind versus true wind is of considerable importance to sailors. Understanding apparent wind, and using it to advantage in setting sails to get the most out of a boat, is a complex subject. We shall not presume to discuss sailing tactics, but we will talk about true wind.

True wind is the actual wind blowing over the surface. Apparent wind is the air flow that strikes a boat in motion. As long as the boat is moving, true and apparent winds will always be different. Normally, apparent wind comes from a point forward of true wind. If the boat is sailing directly into or away from the wind, only velocity will be affected. Ships carry anemometers on their yardarms, but small boats rely on small flags or strips of cloth on the masthead for apparent wind.

On aircraft carriers at sea, true wind is a matter of more than passing interest. In launching and landing aircraft, the ship has to head into the wind. The manuever must be executed smartly, especially if several ships are in formation. It is the job of the carrier's meteorologist to advise the captain of the new course so that he will not have to search for the wind. The weatherman usually rigs up a plotting board of some sort to compute true wind using apparent wind and ship's course and speed. But even when exercising the utmost care, it is tough to nail down true wind direction within 10 degrees. A quicker and often more accurate method —although one that requires practice—is to gauge the wind by appearance of the sea. This is easier to do from the bridge of a ship than from a small boat because of the panoramic view. Aboard ship, the alidade is used to line up wind streaks and the direction of tumble of small wind waves.

Estimating Wind Speed

Estimating wind speed is a bit trickier. Admiral Beaufort's scale is a good foundation to begin on. As experience mounts, judging velocity may be refined down to a knot or two. Enough of the Beaufort Scale to interest boatmen is given here.

BEAUFORT WIND SCALE

Beaufort Number	Wind Speed In Knots	Seaman's Term	Weather Bureau Term	Signs
0	Less than 1	Calm	Light	Water like a mirror. Smoke rises vertically.
1	1 to 3	Light air	Light	Ripples on water. Smoke drifts lazily.
2	4 to 6	Light breeze	Light	Small wavelets. Crests have a glassy appearance and do not break. Wind felt on face.
3	7 to 10	Gentle breeze	Gentle	Large wavelets. Few scattered whitecaps. Wind extends light flag.
4	11 to 16	Moderate breeze	Moderate	Longer wind waves. Frequent whitecaps.
5	17 to 21	Fresh breeze	Fresh	Moderate waves, taking a long form. Many whitecaps; some spray. "Oil" streaks.
6	22 to 27	Strong breeze	Strong	Large waves form. Extensive whitecaps, with flying spray. Small craft warnings hoisted.
7	28 to 33	Moderate gale	Strong	Seas heap up. Foam streaks. Upper limit small craft warnings.

Sailboat races are often won by the crew that is the most weatherwise or windwise, if you will. Sizing up wind conditions in the immediate vicinity is important, but even more so is the ability to recognize wind change ahead of time. We are speaking now of local wind variation, not major shifts due to frontal passages.

During periods of gustiness, "cat's paws" may be seen racing over the water, and the direction of wind shift and gust speed can be readily estimated from them. There is usually time for an alert coxswain to avoid the consequences by letting go the sheets, if the gust is expected to be too much for the boat. Or if he wants to take advantage of the gust, he can trim the sails for the new wind.

An edge over competing boats can sometimes be had by watching other sailboats to windward. Note the sail they are carrying and how they heel. Also, look for smoke from stacks on shore. The shape and direction of the plume can give forewarning of a change in wind.

Study the wind traces in Figures 24–29. Get to know what the "standard deviation" (a weatherman's term) of direction is for each wind type. Knowing this might prevent a serious jibe sometime, if you are prone to sail a little too close on the wind. Or a stable wind might allow you to trim a bit better than a more cautious opponent, and win the race. And that is what you would call a real sailor's wind!

Chapter 8

The Small Craft Sailor and the Restless Sea

The restless, troubled sea has always held a fascination for man, whether he be a wide-eyed landsman viewing the vast expanse for the first time, or a salty old shellback who has spent a lifetime on the realm of Davy Jones.

The newcomer is impressed by even the gentlest surf and, perhaps, puzzled by the process that makes the waves heave up suddenly at the water's edge to tumble into breakers. He may think that the life of these waves is short, indeed. After all, they appear to form just offshore, by some mysterious process, and a few seconds later to die in a harmless rush of foam on the strand.

The experienced mariner knows better. He understands that most waves travel great distances, wending their way effortlessly over hundreds, even thousands, of miles of sea before breaking into surf on some distant beach.

The huge combers that lash the west coast of the United States might have been churned up by gales howling over the cold waters of the Pacific Ocean, far to the northwest, or they could have journeyed across the entire breadth of the Pacific, from the seas near Japan. On a few occasions, swells rolling into California are known to have come from the South Seas, below the equator.

What causes these silent travellers of the seas, and how can they exist so long in an environment fraught with obstacles? And there are many obstacles. Rain, snow, hail, ice all tend to smother the wave form. Opposing winds, though light in force, can all but destroy a wave train. Shallow reefs and small islands sap the strength of great swells so that many sheltered coasts are protected.

In spite of their power, ocean swells are often delicate structures. They exist in form only, without substance. They must constantly advance. To stop moving means certain death. The energy form of the wave, propelled by gravity, rolls through the sea, inhabiting any one parcel of water for just a few seconds. The water mass does not move with them until they become breakers on a beach. If it did, ocean travel would be impossible. Ships could not steam against such walls of water.

Fig. 31. Breakers on the Shore Originate As Wind Waves Hundreds of Miles at Sea

Ocean Waves

Ocean waves begin as little ripples. If the wind blows long enough and strong enough, they grow into giant seas that can break ships in two. This has happened many times. In an Okinawan typhoon of 1945, the heavy cruiser, *Pittsburgh*, lost 150 feet of her bow to a gigantic wave.

The ultimate size of the seas depends upon the strength of the wind and the length of the fetch, that area of ocean affected by the wind. Several days under a raging gale and over a several-hundred mile fetch are needed to build up the largest waves, and, even then, it is difficult for the wind to push the tons of water in a giant wave higher than 35 or 40 feet. An additonal deterrent is that the brute force of the wind actually blows the tops off when they rear too high. Weather observers on Navy hurricane reconnaissance aircraft determine wind speed by the appearance of the sea. The method used is based on the amount of white foam on the sea surface. This foam is actually shattered wave tops. At wind velocities greater than 110 knots, the sea is an almost unbroken mass of white foam.

But in spite of the 40-foot "limit," deep water sailors have long told of nightmarish swells encountered in distant seas. The captain of the *Ascanius*, on a winter run from Japan to Seattle, estimated waves in a severe storm to be 70 feet high. A French officer reported seas of 100 feet near the "Screeching Sixties" between the Cape of Good Hope and the Antarctic Continent. But the greatest wave ever seen—and accepted as fact by oceanographers—was in the central Pacific Ocean, west of Midway Island.

One wild winter night in 1933, as the moon shone through flying clouds ripped to rags by gale force winds, the officer of the deck of the *U.S.S. Ramapo* looked aft to see a huge swell looming above the ship. He noted that the crest was in line with a crossbar on the mainmast. At the moment, the ship was level, in the trough of the sea. The great wave slid under the *Ramapo*, lifting it vertically as if it were weightless. Later, in port, it was possible to calculate the height of the swell. It had measured 112 feet.

Such outsized waves result when two or more seas, moving at different velocities, briefly join to rear skyward into mountainous masses of water. Other outsized waves, "tidal waves," occasionally make news because of the damage caused by them, but these occur infrequently.

Tidal Waves

There are two types of tidal waves, neither of which has anything to do with tide. It is understandable how the misnomer occurred. Unlike wind-wave breakers, the water surge of the tidal wave behaves more like an abrupt monstrous incoming tide. That is because of the immense length of the wave form.

The storm tide of severe tropical hurricanes is a product of the wind, but is quite different from a storm surf. It is a virtual wall of water, built up by hurricane winds. When the wind direction shifts suddenly, this water mass is released to charge into defenseless lowlands. The 1935 Florida Keys disaster, in which hundreds were drowned, was of this nature.

Seismic sea waves, the other tidal wave type, spread out from deep sea earthquakes. The parent quake on the ocean floor goes unnoticed and even on the open sea, the extremely long (several hundred miles) length and low (a foot or two) height of the speeding wave prevent it from being detected by ships' crews. These tremendous swells travel at astounding velocities. The explosion of Krakatoa volcano, near Sumatra, dispatched waves across the Pacific that swept along at 400 knots. On reaching shallow water, the wave shortens and becomes proportionately steeper. Then it grows into a mighty wall and rushes ashore, sometimes inundating land areas with as much as fifty feet of water.

But why should this concern the small craft operator? Few boat-owners contemplate—even in the safety of an armchair—taking their craft into the Screeching Sixties, the Roaring Forties, or the wild winter seas of the North Pacific. True, but a sailor worth his sea legs, no matter how small the boat he captains, is not content to remain in quiet inland waters always. He wants to head out through the inlet, to experience the rhythmic heave of deep sea swells, to feel the sting of salt spray flung at his face by a brisk sea wind. And well he should. The sailor is most at home on the sea, even if he stays within sight of land.

The boatman must understand the causes and character of sea waves and surf to act intelligently in unexpected situations. Suppose he finds himself seaward of an inlet just closed over by breakers. A knowledgeable skipper, when faced with such a case, would heave to, analyze the problem, and devise a plan of action. Normally, that would save the day, because most surfs, whether breaking on a beach or in an inlet, can be navigated.

Wind Waves

The only waves of concern to boatmen are those generated by the wind. Wind waves form whenever air moves over a water surface, whether it be a gentle breeze across a backyard swimming pool or a howling gale over an expanse of ocean. Choppy white caps appear first but, as the wind continues, the waves become higher and longer, developing into "seas." The direction and velocity of these seas is dependent on the wind that generated them. Their direction is the same as the wind, but when the wind shifts, the seas already formed continue to advance on their original course. In a storm where wind direction is changing frequently, such as in a tropical disturbance, many wave trains are sent out from the source.

The subject of sea waves is so complex, and so replete with exceptions to the rule, that to generalize is to invite the scorn of oceanographers. But it is safe to set down a few thumb rules. It might be said, for instance, that the speed of newly formed seas is roughly half the wind velocity. As the waves grow older, they become longer and soon are moving as fast as, or faster than, the wind that made them.

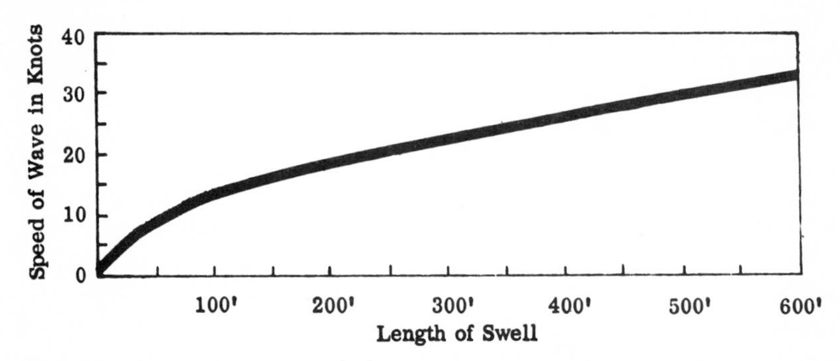

Fig. 32. Relationship of Wave Length to Wave Velocity in Deep Water

Sea Swells

Another generalization may be made concerning the maximum height of waves on the open sea. Wave height, in feet, will be about 2 percent of the square of the wind velocity in knots. Thus, a 10-knot breeze can stir up waves no larger than 2 feet, regardless of duration.

When gale force or hurricane winds bellow across the ocean, they churn up confused masses of waves. Not all of these seas are of the same size, because of the constant shifting of wind direction and gustiness of velocity. Particularly in hurricanes, short, violent squalls race over the water, building up groups of seas higher than the average.

As the wave trains work out of the storm area, a surprising amount of order evolves. The seas become swells and a consistent spacing of waves in the train takes place. The swells flatten, lengthen to a half-mile or more, and go on for great distances. The occasional larger waves, created by travelling squalls, retain their identity. It was partly because of these overgrown swells that seafarers of old claimed that every ninth wave was a troublemaker.

Deep sea swells have an average length-height ratio of 50:1, although the steepness may vary a lot, depending on the age of the wave train. Very old swells often reach 1000:1.

As the wave train glides into shallow coastal water, changes take place in the speed of advance and the swell shape. The waves become slower, shorter, and steeper as they "feel bottom." This happens at a point where the water is one half as deep as the wave length. Finally, the swells reach a critical steepness ratio of 7:1 and they tumble into surf.

Let us take a typical ocean swell and see what happens to it in the shoaling process. It is 100 feet long, 5 feet high, and is moving at 13 knots. Our swell, of course, is only one of many in a train that was generated far offshore. When the sea swell reaches the 8-fathom depth (half the wave length), it begins to change form slightly. The wave length is shortened, but wave height remains the same and, sometimes, increases a bit.

When the altered wave advances into shoal water where the depth is 10 percent of the original swell length (10 feet in this instance), it has reached the outer breaker line. Breakers may form here, or even seaward of this line if there is a strong onshore wind, or if the bottom contour rises abruptly. Usually, the "plunge point" is closer to shore than the "10 percent depth." A thumb rule often stated is that breakers form in water that is as deep as they are high. This rule has been criticized, but it suffices as a rough approximation. A more realistic figure is water depth that is 1.3 times swell height. Oceanographers, in studying the depths at which waves crest, have found that breakers can form in water that is only 0.72 the height of the wave, or as much as twice as deep as the wave is high.

But to return to our hypothetical wave. At a depth of about 1 fathom, the swell has shortened and steepened so that it cannot maintain its form and it topples into a breaker. Momentum causes the breaking top to fall ahead. Now the water mass is actually transported forward. Until this stage, the wave form merely slid through the water. From here on, the breaker decreases in size and velocity and spreads into a "wave of translation," a foaming front of water moving slowly. Our breaker, as a wave of translation, will be 2 feet high and advance at 4 knots.

Surf conditions vary a great deal along various sections of a coastline. The terrain of the coastal shelf is important. Deep water extending right in to the shore, with no outer reefs, is needed to produce good breakers. An example of a radical difference in a short stretch is found on the Georgia and northern Florida coasts. The Atlantic Ocean's westernmost extension on the U. S. shoreline is at Georgia. Here, the northeast longshore currents bypass the beaches due to the sharp cut-in of the coast, and mud and sand have accumulated far offshore for many years. Deep sea waves advancing shoreward are knocked down miles at sea. For the most part, only short wind waves break on Georgia beaches.

Fifty miles to the south, however, the coast curves eastward, and longshore currents keep the shelf swept clean of silt. Sea swells find no obstructions and end up in booming rollers on the north Florida beaches.

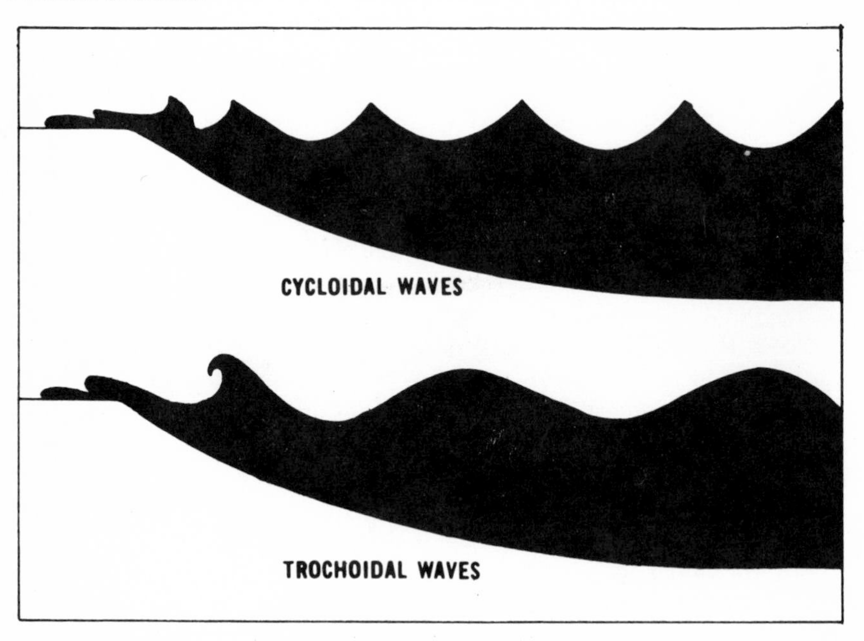

Fig. 33. Types of Ocean Waves

The character and size of a surf depends more on the length of deep sea swells than on their height. Long, low swells, when approaching shoal water, "telescope" to a greater extent than shorter swells and the resulting breakers are brawnier. The water peaks up more when the long swell shortens in the breaking action.

Before leaving deep sea swells to discuss breakers, let us consider the two basic shapes of swells, trochoidal and cycloidal (Figure 33). Trochoids are usually old, long swells that have flattened from wind waves. They offer no problems to small craft in deep water but, as breakers, the trochoids can be quite formidable. Cycloids are short, choppy wind waves, or recently formed swells. Certainly more annoying to make way through, these cycloids, if large, are often dangerous to boats.

Breakers

Breaking waves also come in two distinct types: plunging and spilling. The plungers result from long ground swells (trochoids) that telescope on meeting a steep rise in the ocean floor. They rear up suddenly at the plunge point and fall in a ponderous crash of water, frequently trapping air in the smother of water. This type, obviously unpleasant for boats, makes a noisy surf.

Fig. 34. Plunging Type Breaker on the North Carolina Coast

The "spillers" are gentler waves. They break gradually, with a small crest of white water spreading evenly down the wave. These breakers are caused by shorter sea swells that do not alter much on shoaling. They may be from short trochoids or from cycloidal waves. An easy slope to the shore induces the swells to crest more slowly. However, a steeply sloping coastal shelf can develop a plunging surf even from short swells.

Fortunately for boatmen, breakers in inlets and over offshore bars are normally of the spilling type. This is because inlets and bars, even if shallow, retain enough water depth to prevent the waves from "completely breaking." There is a finality to plunging type breakers on a beach as they expend themselves in one last burst of energy. This is usually not true in inlets.

Fig. 35. A Spilling Breaker

Actually, almost all navigable inlets have a breaker-free channel, however winding and obscure it may be. Only under extreme conditions of heavy swell approaching from seaward, or high winds, does it close over.

It should be kept in mind that breakers caused by shoaling sea swells and breaking wind waves are distinctly different. Wind waves can be annoying, troublesome, or downright dangerous to small boats, depending on the velocity of the wind. But wind waves are directly associated with the wind of the moment, so here the boatman has a measuring stick to determine whether or not he should be cruising. Skill in handling a boat in wind waves is a matter of simple seamanship. On the other hand, negotiating surf requires an additional knowledge of the character of breakers, and it is in this area that we are now delving.

Surf around inlets depends on two things: the size of the approaching sea swell and the bottom contours of inlet floor and reefs. Any boatman can size up the situation by comparing the height and wave length of the oncoming sea swells with the depth of the inlet. Remember the rule that breakers will normally form when the swells reach water that is a little deeper than their height. But also remember that the waves can crest at a depth twice their height, if there is a strong pushing wind and if a tide is flowing against the swells.

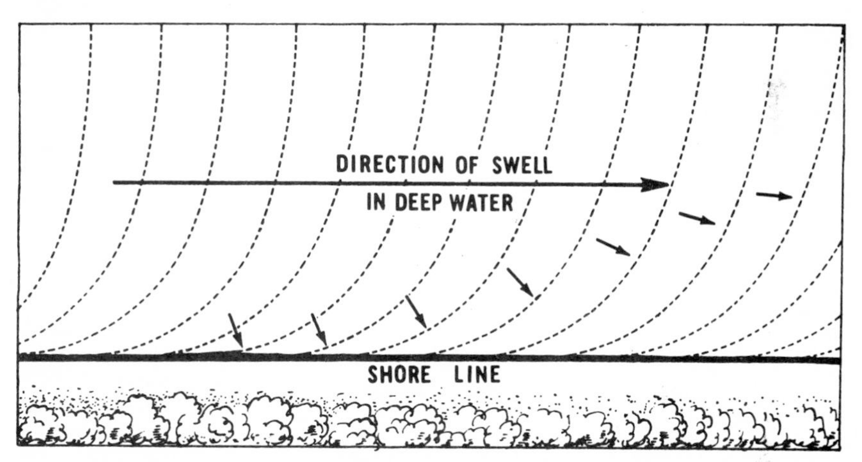

Fig. 36. Refraction of a Wave Train As It Approaches a Coast

The stage and set of the tide greatly affects surf characteristics. When the tide is low, waves are apt to break on offshore bars, thus offering some protection to the shore. At high water, swells sweep in over submerged reefs to break close to shore. Boats passing through inlets find the going easier at high tide because most shoals are covered by water deep enough to inhibit surf. Tide stage on ocean beaches actually affects breaker size. It is usual for the sea floor to slope more steeply above the low water mark than below it. Therefore, high water surf is more abrupt in its formation and the waves are bigger.

Obviously, all invading wave trains do not approach every beach head-on. Sea swells come from many directions, depending on the location of their parent disturbance. But, by the time the waves have become breakers, they do, indeed, roll straight into the strand, or nearly so. This is due to "refraction," the process by which the inshore ends of swells are slowed in their advance by the shoaling bottom. The deep water ends continue their faster pace and the result is a gradual bending around of the wave form. This is illustrated in Figure 36. Here the wave train offshore is actually moving in a direction parallel to the shoreline.

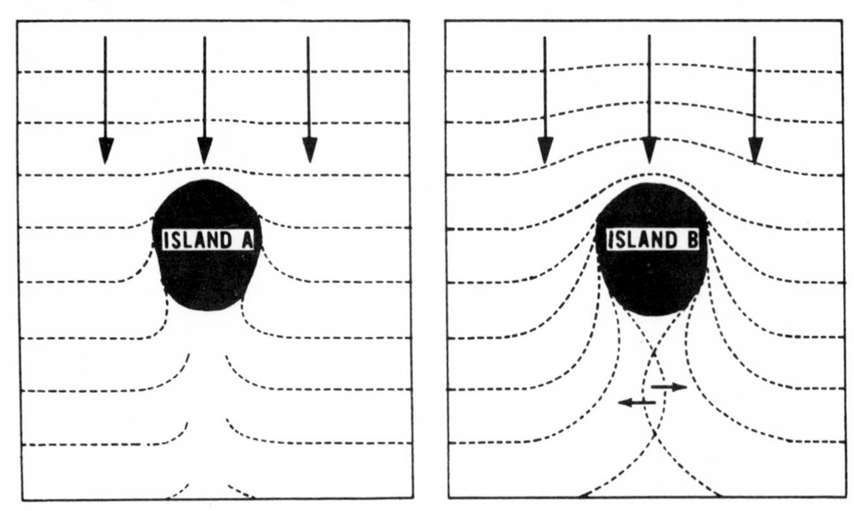

Fig. 37. Wave Trains Passing Islands With Different Shelf Characteristics. Island "A" Has a Steep Shelf. Island "B" Has a Gently Sloping Shelf.

Swells of long wave length are refracted much more than younger, shorter waves. The older swells slow down more rapidly on reaching shoal water.

Refracted waves are "stretched out"—expanded sideways—and because of this, are reduced in size. Their energy is expended over a longer distance. This loss of height may be as much as 50 percent if the sea swell is a long one and if the angle of refraction is 75 degrees or more. Those planning amphibious assault landings seriously consider this fact in selecting beachheads. Refraction of swells on the bordering shores of harbor entrances often is responsible for smooth conditions just inside the harbor, even though it is well exposed. This is especially true in the case of a bay with long, curved shores forming its sides. The destruction of waves by refraction can be complete in this instance.

The real key to the amount of wave refraction is the terrain of the ocean floor near the land in question. Swells advancing at an angle to a steep, rocky coast will be refracted very little, whereas those travelling onto a sloping shelf are bent around to a large degree. Figure 37 pictures wave trains approaching two circular islands. One island has an abrupt drop-off along its shores, while the floor surrounding the other island falls off gradually. Waves sweep past the steep-edged island, but are refracted almost completely around the gently-sloped one.

The presence of an island so affects wave trains that, for long distances to leeward, sea swells are calmed noticeably. Polynesian canoe explorers use this feature to navigate to destinations out of their sight.

Surf and Swell

It is beyond the scope of this book to teach seamanship, but the technique of surf running in powerboats is so vitally dependent on an intimate knowledge of surf and swell that it is well to talk about it briefly.

Every small craft sailor should be prepared to take his boat through the breakers, either inbound or outbound. He may never have occasion to do so, but even the most cautious seaman can lose contact with a winding channel and be forced to go through surf breaking on a bar. The outboard operator may need to beach his boat for one reason or another. The same technique applies to both exigencies. Working in an inlet is, by far, the easier of the two. For one thing, there is more sea room in the inlet, and sea room is mighty important. You will need it, particularly when heading out.

Let us put you, the reader, in a boat, and guide you through a line of breakers. You are now a mile offshore. When you came out of the inlet this morning, the tide was high and the rather heavy swell rolling in from seaward passed through the channel without cresting. But now the tide is low and a fresh onshore breeze has sprung up. The ground swells seem to have become larger. As you approach the inlet, you see that they are breaking in the channel. Don't panic; just lie off and survey the situation.

The wind has stirred up a rash of tumbling whitecaps, but the underriding swell is only too apparent. The boat heaves up under each passing swell and you lost sight of the shore for a few moments in the trough. You feel a bit uneasy. These are big ones! Actually, the breakers in the channel do not appear to be very brawny. But be careful, they never do. The view of a surf from seaward is misleading. You are looking at the backs of those waves. Their fronts present a different picture.

Estimating Wave Heights

Estimate the height of the swells, from trough to top. The breakers will be approximately that size—maybe bigger. Beginners (even old hands) tend to overestimate wave height. Today they are 7 feet. What is the wave length, that distance between successive swells? That will give you an idea of how much room there will be to operate in between waves. You figure the wave length at 125 feet. That distance will close some as the waves telescope. Now count the time in seconds that it takes each swell to pass. That is the "period" of the wave and it is vital. It tells you their speed of advance. Multiply the period by three to get the wave velocity in knots. Your swells have a 5-second period. So they are travelling at 15 knots. They will slow down suddenly after breaking to a speed of 12 knots or so. Breakers will begin in about 11 feet of water today because of the onshore wind and ebbing tide.

Ease the throttle forward and head for the channel—you are going in. Go straight in, at right angles to the wave axis. Slowly at first. Let a couple of swells pass under to gauge their speed and then pick a big one. Big waves travel faster and are not likely to be overtaken. Follow it in. Remain behind it, a quarter of the distance to the next swell. If you keep up with the wave ahead, you will be making 15 knots now and it will feel like 50. The water rushes by and it is turbulent. The boat swerves. Steering is difficult, but take care. You must keep her under control. To broach before the following sea would be serious. You must not overrun the wave ahead. You could be drawn into it and pitchpoled end-over-end.

By now, the wave ahead has broken and a mass of bubbling foam races past you. This can be confusing. You may think you are in the breaker itself. Stand by to reduce speed! Ease off handsomely, watching the wave behind as well as the one ahead. Now the rollers are flattening and going slower. The one ahead has disappeared. You are in the still water of the inlet. You made it! In beaching an outboard under these conditions, you would find that by the time you were in water too shallow to operate in, the waves of translation would be small enough not to present a problem and the boat could be handled manually.

Running seaward through surf is tricky business. Unless the boat is large enough to beat through the breakers, then it should be fast enough to retreat before them, if necessary. Go over all lines of waves of translation. There may be several of these and they increase in size toward the breaker zone. When you can venture no farther through the waves, heave to and watch the outer surf line. There will occasionally be lulls in the breakers, offering a clear path seaward. If the distance through these paths is not great, take advantage of them. Otherwise, watch for rollers that do not extend sideways more than a few hundred feet. These are common. Run parallel to a breaker, going over the unbroken end. But be ready to retreat shoreward should your "hole" close over.

Wind waves in restricted waters never develop beyond the elemental form of the short cycloid. Because of this, they are a nuisance to small craft. Some lakes and bays have fetches long enough to allow fair-sized swells to evolve, but in most of these bodies, the water is shallow. This dampens the action of long ground swells by putting a "floor" under them. Under prolonged gales, 6-foot wind waves have been generated in large sounds on the U. S. east coast. The weather shores of the Great Lakes are pounded by heavy wind waves occasionally.

Be Aware of Wind Velocity

The fresh-water sailor who infrequently operates on the coast is likely to be awed by the whole subject of waves and surf. Certainly he should respect the sea, but to fear it needlessly is to rob himself of much pleasure. There always seems to be an Old Salt around the docks to add to the newcomer's cares by telling of how rough certain stretches of local waters can be. No doubt his advice is well-founded, but the boatman should learn to reason why, and be his own state-of-sea forecaster.

To become rough, bays and sounds must have wind to churn them. It is that simple. The degree of roughness is directly dependent on the velocity of the wind and the fetch. A wind of less than 15 knots, to pick an arbitrary figure, can hardly be of concern to small boats. Recall a statement made earlier in this chapter: the maximum wave that a 10-knot wind can generate is 2 feet in height. And this is with a very long fetch. They will usually be smaller.

Keep Well Informed

When sections of sounds and inlets acquire a bad reputation, it is due to a combination of shallow shoals, strong tidal flow, and openness to the wind. This does, indeed, give rise to choppy water. But a close study of local charts will divulge these areas.

It makes for interesting reading to tell of large, thundering surfs attacking rocky shores. It is romantic. One dreams of shipwreck and high adventure. The fact is, these are rare on most shores, and certainly so on the American east coast. A recent report by the Corps of Engineers cites statistics of surf size along the U. S. shoreline. On beaches of the middle Atlantic coast, for example, breakers average less than 3 feet in height for 50 percent of the time. Only during 10 percent of the year do they exceed 4 feet. West coast surfs are rougher because the prevailing westerly winds of the Pacific send out long wave-length trains. Even so, California rollers remain under 4 feet in height for 75 percent of the time.

Cautious seamen should be cheered by the fact that when really dangerous surfs are rolling in, it is almost always under the fury of active storms, usually winter storms. With the excellent forecast and warning services now available, there is little excuse for not being ashore before trouble strikes.

The Navy Hydrographic Office has studied sea and swell conditions prevailing over the oceans of the world and conclusions reached show that, in cruising areas usually frequented by yachtsmen, seas run high more infrequently than would be expected. On the Atlantic, from the equator northward to 50 degrees latitude, low seas (under 3 feet) can be expected 50 percent of the time in summer. Seas higher than 8 feet occur about 5 percent in summer. These mean heights and percentages vary in favor of the yachtsman in many places, such as the Gulf of Mexico and the Caribbean, where the long fetches of open ocean are broken by land masses. Caribbean sea swells average "low" 70 percent of the summer, and these frequencies are despite the occasional severe hurricanes that plow through these sections.

Summer is the quietest season, of course. As winter wears on, things churn up more, especially at the higher latitudes. In tropical waters, the change is less dramatic and low seas still hold for 40 percent or more of the time during the winter months.

This is not to say that the small craft sailor may roam the deep blue with impunity, but it is well to keep in mind that the sea is usually well-behaved. It rears its back only with cause. Tropical storms and itinerant low pressure areas are cause enough, but the well-informed sailor of today can keep track of these disturbances and stay out of trouble.

He can stay out of trouble, that is, if he has a basic understanding of the sea and what makes it tick, and can apply that knowledge to his everyday boat handling.

Chapter 9

Huracan, The Evil Wind

The northeast trades, steady and strong, swept over the expanse of the tropical Atlantic Ocean, from the African coast to the West Indies. The date was October 1, 1954, and, by rights, the trade winds should have been slackening, for it was getting late in the season. As a matter of fact, the Azores-Bermuda *high*, centered at 30 N and 36 W, had a rather weak central pressure of 1020 millibars. Nevertheless, the trade flow—outward from and counterclockwise around the *high*—held up well. It was a clean flow. The air was bright with excellent visibility. White cumulus clouds floated against a rich blue sky.

Ships on the runs from New York to Capetown and South American ports reported fine weather in the trades to the north of the equator. Surface winds were ENE 18 knots, enough to splatter the blue water with whitecaps. A medium-length sea swell of 185 feet, typical of the trade belt, moved with the wind. The wave period was 6 seconds.

But 700 miles to the east, weather was making up. The SS *African Trader*, from Accra to New York, steamed into an area of heavy cumulus shortly after midnight on October 1. Actually, the weather was not unusual enough to arouse suspicion. The officer of the watch thought nothing of the few rain showers about. They were light and had none of the squall-like characteristics of pre-hurricane weather. The wind blew an unwavering 20 knots from the east and the ocean rolled on in a way that any sailor would recognize as "trade sea." The barometer was normal.

The Ominous Easterly Wave

So, the *African Trader's* coded weather report was beat out on the wireless and treated as routine. Treated as routine by everyone except the meteorologists on duty at the Weather Bureau Hurricane

Forecast Center in San Juan, and the Weather Bureau and Navy Hurricane Centers in Miami. To these men, the observation represented a departure, however small, from the constant trade flow. They noted the cumulus congestus clouds, the showers, and the slight veering in wind direction. Almost as one, they drew a short orange line, oriented north-south, on their weather maps. The line ran through the *African Trader's* position at 22 N and 31 W, and for several hundred miles to the south. This was an easterly wave.

To forecasters concerned with weather in the tropics, the easterly wave is as familiar as the isobars that make up their weather maps. The people of Florida and the islands of the Caribbean know about easterly waves. Even small boys in Miami have been overheard discussing them intelligently. Their interest is well-founded, because the easterly wave is the mother of hurricanes. At least 80 percent of all Atlantic hurricanes are spawned in easterly waves. A similar number of Pacific typhoons come about in the same manner.

The idea of the easterly wave is fairly recent. In the late 1930's, Gordon Dunn, now Director of the National Hurricane Center in Miami, noticed that a pattern of westward-moving atmospheric waves progressed over the tropical Atlantic and Caribbean. These waves were several hundred miles in length and each contained a weak pressure trough. There were wind shifts associated with them, and rain showers and thunderstorms. They ran through the trades from May through November of each year and were most frequent from June to September. They were called "waves in the easterlies," or easterly waves.

It might be explained to the non-meteorologist that weather features in the tropics are much more subtle and difficult to detect on weather maps than their counterparts of higher latitudes. Forecasters accustomed to analyzing maps containing well-defined fronts, and *highs,* and *lows,* find tropical analysis elusive and dull, when first introduced to it. Even skilled meteorologists have a tough time locating easterly waves until they have been around the tropics for a while. So, the easterly wave took a longer time to be discovered than did, for instance, cold and warm fronts.

For the most part, tropical weather analysis is difficult because of the lack of strong temperature contrasts between air masses. Certainly in summer, and to a lesser extent in winter, there are no cold or dry air masses roaming around. All of the air in the tropics is the same—Tropical Maritime. There are differences in batches of *mT* air, but they are slight and usually occur, not at the surface

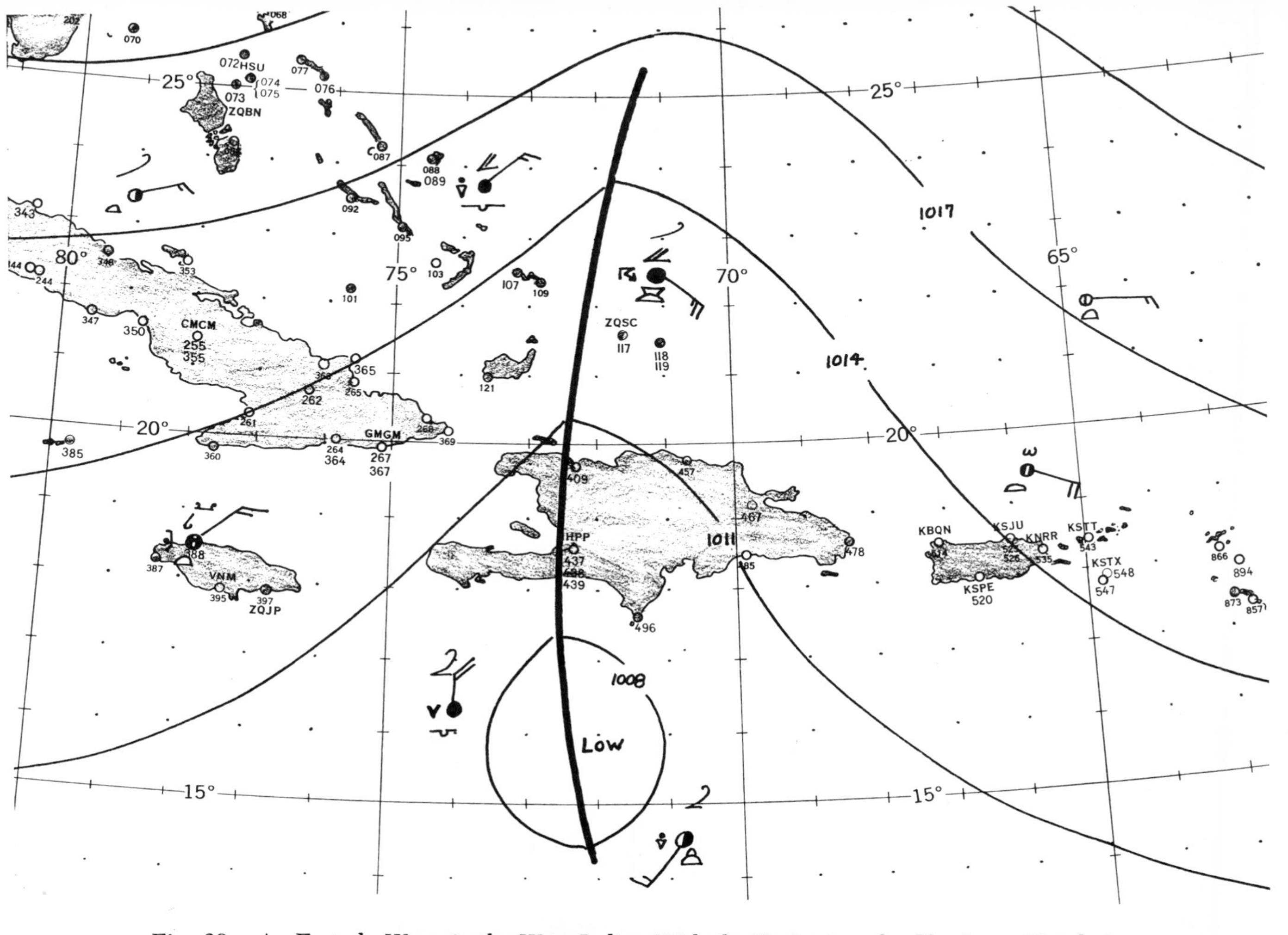

Fig. 38. An Easterly Wave in the West Indies, With the Beginning of a Hurricane Circulation

where the unchanging sea leaves its mark on all that touches it, but at higher levels. Often, weak easterly waves cannot be detected at the surface, even by old hands, but can be picked out readily after close scrutiny of pressure-height variations a few thousand feet up.

It can be said that tropical weather, like a sleeping tiger, is gentle, soft and quiet, but when awakened, the trouble-potential is terrific. It is a tribute to that mighty-mite of the atmosphere, water vapor, that the terrifying energy exhibited in hurricanes comes from one source: high humidity of tropical air. For it is water vapor alone that furnishes the fuel for the hurricane-machine.

The easterly wave is really an imperfection in the smooth flow of the trade winds. Unlike fronts, there is no contrast in air properties on either side of the wave. The wind shift is slight, usually from ENE to E or ESE, as the wave moves westward over a station. The fluctuation in barometric pressure is negligible. But these changes, however meager, cause important developments in weather conditions. Copious water vapor is responsible.

Origin of Easterly Waves

The origin of easterly waves is still a bit obscure. The principal cause seems to be a surging of the mid-ocean semi-permanent *highs*. Recall that these high pressure areas, in the Atlantic and Pacific, are fed by air settling earthward from the general circulation. The centers of these *highs* roam in well-defined orbits, and when the movement equator-ward is combined with an increase in pressure, a strong impulse is given to the trade winds. The surging of the trade flow sets off an easterly wave that moves westward. Occasionally, the dangling end of an old cold front that has penetrated deep into the tropics will be broken off and carried as an easterly wave in the trade winds.

Prevalence of Easterly Waves

There is at least one wave in the easterlies present over some part of the Caribbean and tropical Atlantic every day during the summer months. The islands of the Antilles can expect a wave passage twice a week at this season. Obviously, all of these are not hurricane brewers. Each easterly wave has its own personality and only one in four can be classed as unstable. Weathermen learn to recognize the troublemakers by such characteristics as whether the rain showers run ahead of the wave (an unstable condition) or only to the rear of it (stable); whether it is moving slower than the trade winds (unstable) or equal to them (stable); whether its upper reaches lean to the west (unstable) or to the east (stable). One thing is certain: whenever the orange line representing an easterly wave is on the map, it is intently watched by forecasters.

Hurricane Alert

And so, on October 2, 1954, the easterly wave, drawn on the basis of the *African Trader's* message of the day before, was under surveillance. In 24 hours, it had advanced 390 miles. At a speed of 16 knots, the wave was going slower than the trade wind component. A ship well ahead of the wave told of cumulo-nimbus clouds and showers. Here were two good indications that it was becoming unstable. Interest quickened.

Forecasters made a check of sea-water temperatures near and ahead of the wave. Their information came from ship weather reports and those of the eastern Caribbean islands. Water temperatures play an important role in hurricane formation. If the water is warm, the heat energy and moisture so needed as fuel for the hurricane-engine are present. A threshold temperature of 80 degrees has been set by researchers. A few hurricanes have been known to spawn in areas where the sea was colder, but these are considered freaks. In fact, the wide variation in the number of hurricanes from year to year has been linked to the temperatures of the oceans. Differences in large-scale wind currents each year control ocean currents to an extent and these, in turn, have a bearing on tropical storm incidence. On October 2, 1954, the sea in the area under suspicion was a warm 82 degrees.

Navy Hurricane Hunter Goes Into Action

During the third of October, the easterly wave churned westward at 18 knots. The Navy Hurricane Hunter's advance unit at San Juan was alerted. The wave was a bit far out for aircraft reconnaissance, but preparations were made to launch a flight next morning.

At dawn on the fourth, the big blue Navy plane took off from San Juan. As it droned southeastward, the Aerologist, perched in the glassed-in nose, glanced around. A few white cumulus clouds floated far below. The Leeward Islands slid by underneath, looking like a string of emeralds against the incredible cobalt blue sheet of the Caribbean. The weather was good here, but off to the south, where the Windward Islands chain stretched out as far as the eye could see, big cumulus tops merged with the distant haze. To the east, a milky cirro-stratus bank fanned out above the horizon, and beneath it were darker clouds.

Two hours later, the Navy plane was in the easterly wave. The air was rough. Towering cumulo-nimbus clouds were all around. Heavy rain showers, like thick grey curtains, hung from the cloud bases to the sea. The dark blue Atlantic was streaked with rolling white horses. The wind was estimated at 35 knots, but as yet there was no organized storm circulation.

The Birth and Christening of Hazel

That afternoon, the barometer took an abrupt spill along the Windward chain. By sundown, the wind at Barbados, the easternmost island of the Antilles, had backed a few points and, although not strong, had a fitful gustiness not normal to the trade winds. The ocean, too, was portending. The breakers rolling into the beach came in larger and less frequently than the trade-wind surf. They were noisy, crashing on the beach with a booming sound. The swell period was now 10 seconds. Natives on the island knew the signs. A tropical storm was forming out there, somewhere to the east. The fading light of the sun shone a sickening yellow on cirrus fingers that pointed seaward.

And so was born terrible-tempered *Hazel*—born at sea, "out there, somewhere to the east" of Barbados. She was destined to become one of the most destructive hurricanes of all time. However, it was not until the next day, October 5, that *Hazel* was christened.

Events broke fast on the fifth. At Barbados, the grey light of dawn revealed heavy strato-cumulus clouds driving in from the sea. The pulsating wind blew from the northeast, gusting to 36 knots. The barometer fell steadily, though not steeply. Powerful waves pounded the beach with a regular cadence. Intermittent squalls swept in with the strange, brief violence found only in pre-hurricane rains.

In the Eye of the Hurricane

From San Juan, a Navy Hurricane Hunter was dispatched to the scene. After fighting its way at low level through turbulent rain squalls, the aircraft, with unexpected suddenness, broke into the ill-defined eye of the storm. The air was hazy, but smooth. The water's surface was a confused mess of cross-seas, peaking and tumbling, as wave trains coming from all sides collided. On the way in, the plane had encountered winds of 78 knots, so the storm more than qualified as a hurricane.

The pilot circled in the eye while the radio operator sent word back telling the story. At the Miami Hurricane Center, the name

Hazel was pulled off the shelf and the storm was officially tagged.

Hazel drifted westward across the Grenadine Islands and into the Caribbean. By the next day, maximum winds had reached 92 knots and on October 7, 102 knots. To think all of this developed from a handful of cumulus clouds in a trade-wind imperfection, an easterly wave!

Why and How Do Hurricanes Form?

What happened? How could such violence spring from a tropical atmosphere that is renowned for its gentleness? What did the easterly wave have to do with it?

We will begin by putting our cards on the table. No one knows exactly why hurricanes form. Intensive research continues, and some of our best scientific minds are at work on the problem, but, so far, success has been limited. Ideas have been produced and, although they are as yet not proved, the solution may be nearer than is realized.

The accepted theory in the past was that in the hot, humid doldrums there would occasionally rise from the sea's surface a great glob of air that would continue upward to form many thunderstorms. These would somehow coalesce into one, and air would rush in from all sides to fill the resulting low pressure area. That was supposed to be the start of the hurricane circulation. This naive theory was abandoned about 25 years ago, although it is found, even today, in some meteorology books.

Triggering Mechanisms

It is understood now that there must be a triggering action. The easterly wave serves this purpose well. There are two other less-important mechanisms: old cold fronts that have stagnated in the tropics and the Intertropic Convergence Zone. The *ICZ*, sometimes called the Equatorial Front, is the boundary zone between the Northern Hemisphere's northeast trades and the southeast trade winds of the Southern Hemisphere.

The *ICZ* is a broad line that snakes about in tropical oceans. Weather is quite nasty where the two trade flows meet head-on. In fact, it was this zone that caused so much trouble, meteorologically speaking, for World War II aviators in the equatorial Pacific.

At any rate, the three triggering mechanisms all have one thing in common. They forcibly lift surface air to great heights. It is this lifting, and resulting expansional cooling, that condenses the air's invisible moisture into clouds, and then into rain. Now all this sounds familiar because it is the same process that causes weather all over the world. But there is a difference in the tropics. Tropical air can hold much more water vapor than that of the temperate latitudes and, to repeat an important fact, the potential energy of copious water vapor cannot be overemphasized. So, when large-scale lifting of humid tropical air takes place, it spells trouble. This trouble comes from the heat generated by the condensation of water vapor. When the heat is released, it makes the rising column of air go up even faster, which in turn condenses more moisture, ad infinitum.

Fig. 39. Trade-wind Air is Dry Above the Lower Layers, So Showers are Sparse

Now something additional is required to start a hurricane circulation out of this simple convection process, but before going into that, let us see exactly how an easterly wave manages to act as the triggering mechanism.

One significant feature of the trade belt—and this will seem odd to the uninitiated—is the dryness of the air above 10,000 feet. This accounts for the lack of rain showers in the trade winds. Trade air is full of puffy cumulus, but the cloud tops evaporate when they push into the dry air layer. One thing an easterly wave does is to force high-humidity surface air to great heights, enabling showers and thunderstorms to form. It does this by convergence, the packing together of air in a horizontal plane so that some of it must shoot upward. This convergence comes about because the low pressure trough of the wave causes the air blowing from the east to turn in a curving counterclockwise pattern, thus allowing the east wind coming in from farther out to pile into it. Old cold fronts in the tropics and the Intertropic Convergence Zone are also loaded with convergence for approximately the same reason.

Hurricanes vs. Typhoons

Although hurricanes and typhoons are of the same breed of cats, there is some difference in their beginnings. This disparity is due to their respective geographical areas and not the storms themselves. The tropical Atlantic is narrow compared to the Pacific, and the *ICZ*, which exhibits itself only over water, is hard to locate in the Atlantic. But, in the other ocean, the *ICZ* is a thing to reckon with, and many typhoons are born in its convergence zone. Far-Eastern meteorologists watch closely when the *ICZ* pokes a nose-like perturbation too far north of the equator. The chances are that a typhoon will pop up when this northward excursion reaches 10 degrees latitude. If an easterly wave is cruising along with the trade flow and will brush against the hump in the *ICZ*, then forecasters begin reaching for the file containing the name of the next typhoon. One is almost certain to go whirling away from this junction, the famous "triple point" of Father C. E. Depperman, Philippine typhoon authority.

Another can't-miss situation arises when an easterly wave walks into an old cold front. This combination has been the fuse that fired off a number of hurricanes.

So, once the humid tropical air has been lifted and surface moisture has been carried aloft, then what? Some additional unusual conditions must prevail, or hurricanes would be an everyday occurrence. It is here that the theorists have been on shaky ground, although now they think they understand those conditions. It appears that there must be a high-level anticyclone, say at 40,000 feet, capping the would-be hurricane. The air up there should be cooler than normal. This creates a steep lapse rate. The lower air, warmed first by the sea and later by the heat produced during condensation, whooshes upward in strong drafts. Remember that these updrafts are aided by convergence in the easterly wave, or other triggering device.

The vital ingredient comes in now, and that is the diverging, or outward, flow of air from the upper *high*. This pumps the rising air out and away from the area. If more air is pumped out at the top than enters at the bottom, pressure will fall in the convective core, resulting in a low pressure center. This center sucks in more air at the bottom and the storm engine is cranked up.

Some Hurricane Statistics

That a unique set of circumstances is needed to fire off a storm is illustrated by the small number of hurricanes each year. Considering that easterly waves prowl about the trades quite frequently, the yearly average of eight tropical cyclones is small. In 1890, and again in 1914, only one churned Atlantic waters. The banner year of 1933 saw twenty-one Atlantic hurricanes. Such fluctuations seem to be geared to seasonal changes in sea temperatures and the shape of the general circulation. When the jet stream, for example, is cruising far to the north, hurricanes are more prone to spawn.

September is the hurricane month. August and October are next in storm frequency. Eighty percent of all tropical cyclones occur in these three months. The logic here is that by late summer and early fall sea temperatures are at their highest, and there is more chance of cold northerly currents and anticyclones way up yonder.

While citing statistics, here are a few records set by tropical storms. The average life span of a hurricane is nine days, but *San Ciriaco*, a most troublesome hurricane of 1899, lasted five weeks. The lowest barometer reading ever reliably observed was in the eye of a Pacific typhoon. Near the Philippines, on August 18, 1927, the Dutch ship *Sapoeroea* experienced a pressure of 26.18 inches. The record for the United States—and all land stations, incidentally—was made at Lower Matecumbe Key, Florida, on September 2, 1935. In the center of the notorious Labor Day Storm, the pressure fell to 26.35 inches. It was in this small, violent hurricane, one of the most intense in history, that all-time high winds of 210 knots (estimated, not recorded) were attained.

The word hurricane comes from *huracan*, a Spanish word which originated from various similar terms used by the Caribbean Indians to describe the "devil wind," "storm god," and "evil wind"—all most lurid and apt. Typhoon is a corruption of *tai fung*, from a Chinese dialect, meaning "great wind."

The Dangerous Semicircle

On the sixth of October, 1954, dawn did not break over the southeastern Caribbean. Only a dull greyness oozed out of the black murk to show that night was dead. To the harried skipper of the miserable little motor vessel, *Hermanos*, the faint light of day was small consolation. It revealed a terrifying scene. The boiling, spume-covered sea merged with the frenzied sky. The wind shrieked horribly. Great, rolling waves crashed over the bow of the vessel as she beat her way slowly to the southwest towards Caracas. Two crewmen were nearly washed over the side by a fathom of green water that raked topside. The skipper fought the helm and feared for the life of his ancient tub in the tempestuous seas. Without communication, he had been caught unawares by the storm. Fortunately, the *Hermanos* missed the dangerous semicircle—the northern side—of the hurricane, or she would have gone down with all hands.

At this stage of *Hazel's* life, the dangerous semicircle was the northern half because she was moving to the west. The dangerous semicircle of hurricanes is often referred to by compass azimuth. It is usually said to be that part of the storm toward the northeast. Actually, the position of the dangerous semicircle depends upon which way the cyclone is moving. In the Northern Hemisphere, winds blow counterclockwise around hurricanes, and the wind on the starboard will have added to it the speed of movement of the storm itself, whereas on the port side, this movement will be subtracted from the gradient wind. Another reason is that by the time a hurricane has reached maturity, it is more likely than not to be curving to the right. This results in a tighter packing of pressure on the starboard side, thus increasing the gradient winds. The dangerous semicircle can change in short order, as the direction of the storm changes.

Recurvature

Hazel was moving westward across the Caribbean because she was imbedded in the large-scale trade flow and was being carried with it as a small whirling eddy is carried downstream in a river current. Since almost all tropical storms begin life in the trade belt, the traditional path taken by them is westward at first, later recurving northward.

The recurvature causes meteorologists the most headaches. To forecast the point of recurvature is difficult, and yet just where a storm recurves is of great moment, because this usually determines which section of a coast will be hit, if, indeed, the coast is to be affected at all. Most tropical storms recurve and head out to sea short of populated land areas.

Hurricanes recurve because of two factors. For one thing, as the storm grows in size, its top extends out of the trade flow into the region of westerly winds. But more important is the fact that the vortex drifts to the western limit of the trade belt, and then the wind current in which it is imbedded turns northerly.

It is easy to say that hurricanes merely drift with the major wind patterns and, for the most part, that is true, but it is not quite that simple. Evidence is accumulating that there is some other steering control in the storm itself. However, it is well to look into the upper atmosphere for guidance. The trouble here is that there is scant information on upper winds over the tropics and ocean areas, so forecasting hurricane movement is like playing blindman's buff.

So it was with *Hazel.* She plowed inexorably westward across the Caribbean for three more days. She was wild and woolly, and forecasters knew that the farther she went before recurving, the more risk there was to the United States. Then it happened; recurvature. On October 10, *Hazel* ran out of the trade flow and, steered by a strong southerly current, veered sharply to the north. It appeared that the States would be spared, but that Haiti would catch it. Haiti did.

Hazel Hits Haiti

Hazel crashed into the western tip of the island early on the twelfth. The wind, the sea, and the torrential rains which caused floods and a landslide, resulted in over 400 deaths. Seven-thousand-foot mountains nearly knocked the life out of the storm. Winds dropped to 40 knots.

Hurricanes are creatures of the sea. When they pass over land, the delicate balance between moisture supply and the storm-engine is upset. Death of the hurricane usually follows within a few hours. Mountainous terrain applies an extra brake to the winds, as it did when *Hazel* crossed Haiti. However, a few days later, *Hazel* was to be the classic exception to this rule as she charged up through the eastern United States, wreaking violence as far north as Canada.

Hazel Weakens but Revives

Early on the morning of the thirteenth, *Hazel* was in the Windward Passage, weakened from her bout with Haitian mountains. Meteorologists knew that the ill-health of *Hazel* was only temporary. Water temperatures in the Bahamas were high enough to help her regain strength again, but they began to think that any danger to the mainland was remote. Then some dramatic shifts in the upper wind patterns took place.

Analysts in the Hurricane Centers watched with apprehension as an upper level anticyclone, crouched over the east coast, began wandering seaward. Had this blocking *high* stayed where it was,

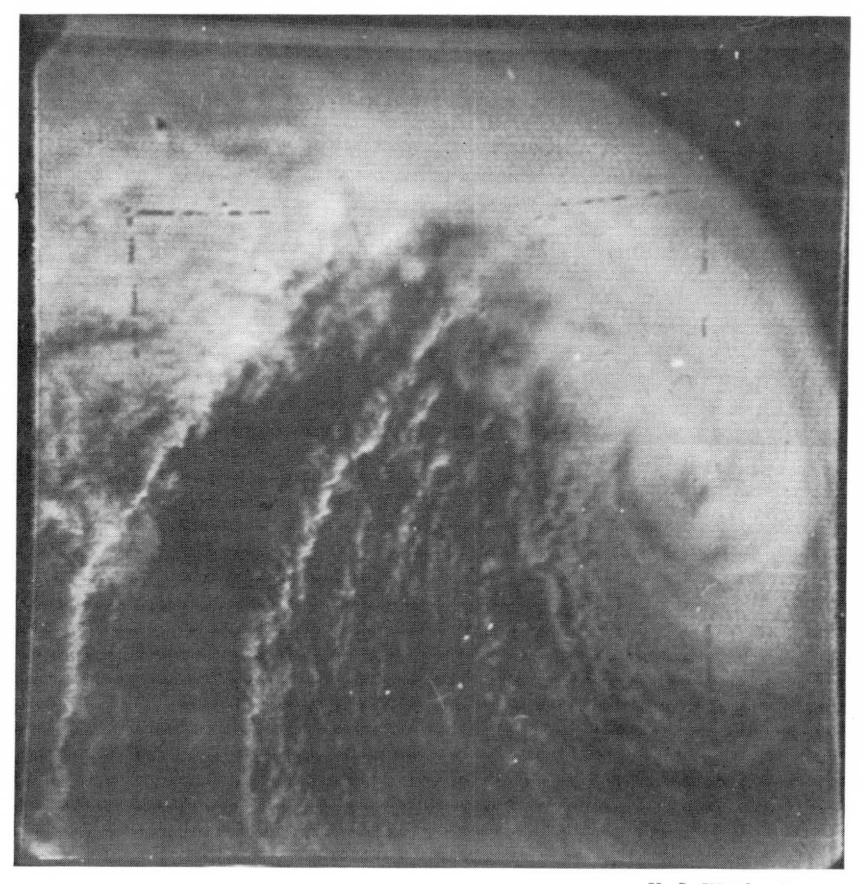

(U. S. Weather Bureau)

Fig. 40. A Pacific Typhoon Discovered by *Tiros* Satellite

the hurricane would have spun harmlessly out into the Atlantic. But now it was being caught up in the easterly air drift around the *high*.

Midday on the thirteenth, the storm recurved again, this time to a northwesterly heading. Ominously, a deep low pressure trough at 19,000 feet was snaking eastward across the United States. Ahead of this trough were accelerating southerly winds. *Hazel* was being drawn into this current and she picked up forward speed. By October 14, she had regained all of her old vigor, and then some. A Hurricane Hunter found winds of 125 knots in her rotating core and saw phenomenal seas beneath her.

The storm was headed straight for the Carolina shoreline, but first it had to cross the heavily-traveled coastal shipping lanes. These ship-routes were loaded, as they usually are, on October 14. Had the shipmasters taken no preventative action to avoid the plundering hurricane, several dozen of the ships would have been clobbered, and probably some destroyed. But it would be difficult to find a seaman who does not make every effort to get out of a hurricane's path. And if the effort is made intelligently, success is almost certain. If it were not for radar and aircraft reconnaissance, seagoing tropical storms would be difficult to track because weather reports from ships near storm centers are sparse.

With today's excellent warning service, there is little need for seamen to do their own weather analysis. Even so, it is well to understand the wind circulation around tropical storms and the paths taken by them. Common sense then dictates the proper course of action.

In the Northern Hemisphere, winds blow counterclockwise around the hurricane (the opposite below the equator), and into the center of low pressure at a 15-degree angle. The closer to the center, the less the angle, until, at the rim of the eye, the wind is howling around parallel to the center, fruitlessly trying to reach the core. Centrifugal force holds it off. For practical purposes, tropical cyclones are considered to be circular. Most of them are.

The Storm Card

Some authorities recommend that a "storm card" be constructed and used to visualize the ship's position relative to the hurricane. A storm card is simply a drawing of the pressure and wind fields of the cyclone, showing the dangerous and navigable semicircles. Even without previous knowledge of the hurricane's position, a good deduction can be made by observing local wind direction and velocity, and barometric pressure. But it is more important to watch the changes that occur in local weather.

Three Ships in Hazel's Path

Let us consider the case of three ships in the sea lanes ahead of *Hazel* on October 14. The northernmost vessel is beginning to feel the effects of the circulation. The glass is falling and the wind is from the east, veering (hauling clockwise) slowly. This means that the ship is on the starboard side of the hurricane; that the dangerous semicircle is approaching. The navigator sets a course of ENE, keeps the wind on the starboard bow, and makes as much way as possible. A sailing vessel would stay closehauled on a starboard tack and get the heck out to the northeast, bearing more to the east and south as the wind permitted.

At the southernmost ship, the wind is north-northeast, backing (shifting counterclockwise). She is on the storm's port side, the navigable semicircle, and certainly wants to stay on that side. To do so, she heads SW with the wind on the starboard quarter, gradually turning more to the south as the wind backs. Under sail, a ship would hold a starboard tack and turn south with the backing wind.

The third ship is directly in the path of *Hazel*. Pressure is falling fast, but the clue is that the northeast wind increases in velocity but does not change direction. The captain knows he must make for the navigable semicircle. He puts the wind two points on the starboard quarter and scampers for safety. A sailing vessel would do the same. In all of the above cases, the skipper would know he was working out of the storm when his barometer began to rise.

Carolinas are Alerted

At sunrise on October 14, *Hazel* was near Great Bahama Island, but precursory signs were beginning to appear on the North Carolina coast, 500 miles away.

"I awoke with a start," said Mrs. Charles Gould. "The room was a blood red. It took a while to realize that the eerie crimson glow was coming through the window. In a matter of minutes, the red changed to orange, then to saffron. The grass, trees, houses, everything, were all the same sickening color. Then it was gone and a dull grey light took over. This was the hurricane-sunrise. I had seen it in Florida, but never quite like this."

The Hurricane-Sunrise

The hurricane-sunrise must be seen to be believed. The scientific reasoning that the sun's rays color the concentrated moisture droplets in the air does not explain why it is unique among all other sunrises or sunsets.

Course of Hazel's Destruction

Along the low, white-sand beaches of the Carolinas, the heavy storm swell was beginning to roll in. At Wrightsville Beach, N. C., the wave period was 16 seconds, indicating that the deep-water swells were 1300 feet long and racing in at 50 knots.

"The breakers could be heard booming on the beach a half-mile away," Mrs. Gould said. "There was an odd silence between each crash—so different from the normally continuous sound of the surf.

Fig. 41. The Tremendous Force of the Sea Took Its Toll As *Hazel* Crashed Into the North Carolina Coast

The waves were coming in from the south-southeast and this was unusual. The wind was freshening from the east and dark clouds flew in from the sea. A higher cloud layer was moving swiftly from the south. I knew then that the storm wouldn't pass offshore as we had hoped."

Indeed, *Hazel* was headed straight for Wrightsville Beach. Entangled in the strong and deep south-southeast current of the upper pressure trough over the United States, she had no other choice. Hurricane warnings were hoisted for North Carolina at 1100, October 14.

This brings up a point. During the past several years, many destructive hurricanes have plunged into the Carolinas and have continued on up the coast to bring grief to other sections of the country not accustomed to tropical storms. This has given rise to scare-articles in magazines and other dark mutterings about how our climate is changing, variously attributed to nuclear explosions, shifting of the Gulf Stream, and tampering with the elements by professional rainmakers. But the fact is, *Hazel* went where she did because she happened along at just the right time to be caught in the high-level wind pattern of the pressure trough. It was strictly a matter of timing. This was true of *Carol*, *Diane*, *Helene*, and other hurricanes of the same era.

Hurricane *Hazel* struck the North Carolina coast at 1030 on October 15, near Ocean Isle Beach. Onshore winds of 125 knots battered the shore and destruction was severe along 200 miles of coastline. Entire communities were wiped out. At Long Beach, 20 miles to the east of the eye, devastation was complete. The island was swept clean. No debris was left. No trace of concrete floors, driveways, or miles of paved road remained.

The Storm Surge

It was not the wind that really did the damage, but the fierce force of the sea. And this is true of most hurricanes. The great storms of history have taken their toll through the work of that irksome phenomenon, the storm surge, in association with pounding by huge breakers.

The storm surge, sometimes called the storm tide or storm wave, is a surge of water that, in its most spectacular form, rushes into an area of the coast much as does a tidal wave. More frequently it is exhibited as a sudden rise in water level. It is caused, first, by the level of the sea rising under the reduced pressure of the cyclone. Water level will rise one foot for each reduction of one inch in barometric pressure. In the case of *Hazel*, this would amount to about two and a half feet. Not much in itself, but when this body of water is heaved ashore by 100-knot winds, and arrives at the time of an abnormally high tide resulting from a full autumn moon, trouble is afloat. Add overriding 20-foot breakers to this and it is small wonder that several thousand buildings were demolished along the Carolina shores on October 15, 1954.

The storm surge occasionally charges into a narrow bay or river as a bore. In 1926, a wall of water destroyed hundreds of boats in the Miami River that had sought refuge from the serious Florida hurricane of that year. In the September, 1935, Florida Keys storm, survivors told of a 20-foot wall of water that came in with the calm center. And in one of the major disasters of the Indian Ocean, the tropical cyclone of 1864, a 40-foot storm wave also came with the eye of the storm. Fifty thousand people were drowned. Other 40-foot storm waves, in which many thousands have lost their lives, have been recorded, but they are rare and, fortunately, seldom affect the United States. It takes a special combination of circumstances to develop storm surges that behave like overpowering tidal waves. Ocean-bottom contour is one of the most important of these.

There are several locations in the United States especially susceptible to an unusual, if more gradual, build-up in water level, however. With sustained, strong northeast winds and high tides, Hampton Roads in Virginia suffers from extreme build-up. A hurricane in August, 1933, approached this section from such a direction to allow onshore winds for a long period. Tides rose seven feet above normal and flooded downtown Norfolk. Long Island Sound, N. Y., experiences an unusual surge pattern under certain conditions of wind direction and velocity.

Hurricanes are receiving a lot of attention nowadays. The detection and warning services are excellent and there is little or no excuse for the yachtsman to be caught at sea with one of the monsters. Actually, there is one potentially dangerous area—the central Gulf of Mexico coast. Occasionally, a tropical storm will form close offshore and move into the beach almost before meteorologists know it is there.

But we have faith in our weatherwise boating friends. We know they will be able to smell trouble and head into a safe harbor in plenty of time.

Chapter 10

Sailor Take Warning?

Because of a red sky in the morning? It would be a pretty good idea, because the air is loaded and, as the old fisherman would say, "The day is a danged weather breeder." The red sky caused by the slanting rays of the rising sun striking a concentration of moisture particles, combined with salt nuclei or dust, is a warning of approaching ill weather.

But what about the rash of other proverbs, the heritage of old saws that have been passed down from generations of seafaring men to enrich our nature lore? For the most part, they are well-founded and do, indeed, tell the weather story. Through the years, men have watched the elements at work and, without understanding the complicated processes that make it so, have discerned a pattern—a master plan—that unfolds with dramatic regularity. And who could be more qualified to develop the "rules" than the sailors who spent their lives being buffeted and blessed by wind and weather?

A few decades ago, however, there came a period when it was thought smart to laugh off all that was considered "old-fashioned." Weather adages came under the gun as scientifically-minded young meteorologists attempted to forecast weather with precision from charts, instruments, and mathematical formulae. If a weatherman looked out the window before issuing a forecast, he invited the scorn of his peers for taking an "emotional approach." But, as these young men grew in experience and wisdom, they learned to gaze skyward more frequently to get the "feel" of the weather. Not that every forecaster mumbled to himself such rhymes as,

Mackerel scales and mares' tails
Make lofty ships carry short sails,

but when he witnessed the graceful, icy fingers of cirrus clouds—mares' tails—racing eastward across the sky, he knew that a strong, high-level wind flow was literally whipping the top off a distant storm area. And, a few hours later, as he saw the modulated patches of cirro-cumulus cloud balls, like stratospheric fish scales, he understood that these westerly winds, six miles up, had formed a high velocity core—a jet stream. The combination of the low pressure center somewhere to the west and the jet stream riding over it meant bad weather.

Read the Signposts

Of course, the forecaster did not need the appearance of the sky to tell him of the low pressure area, or of the jet stream. His weather maps graphically depicted those features. Nevertheless, the sight of nature at work in the weatherman's "laboratory" gave him a little extra insight, that all-important feel, much like the "seat-of-the-pants" quality an aviator needs in piloting his aircraft despite a cockpit full of electronic aids.

So it is with the yachtsman. He needs to acquire that feel of the weather. His craft may be loaded down with radio gear for receiving weather reports; he may cruise in constant sight of warning flag staffs; he may carefully study the daily weather map, but he is not a seaman until he learns to read the signposts—the sky, the wind, and the sea. If repeating poetic and fascinating old adages makes the remembering easier, then well and good. And some of them are truly poetic:

When freshly blow the nor'western gales,
Then on courses snug we fly;
Soon lesser breezes will fill the sails,
And royals proudly sweep the sky.

There is a worthwhile lesson in practical meteorology there, too. Northwesterly gales blow only on the western side of a low pressure area and, since most weather systems move from west to east, that means the *low* has passed, moved on. The high pressure that normally follows prompts clear skies and "lesser breezes." So, northwest winds betide good weather—with two exceptions! That first blow after a *low* can be pretty rugged for a while.

First rise after a low,
Squalls expect and more blow.

It will abate steadily, though, as the high pressure moves in. The second exception concerns hurricanes. Hurricanes are scornful of the west-to-east-rule. A northerly gale near a tropical storm means only that the storm center is to the southeast. It could be moving in any direction and, instead of experiencing "lesser breezes," the sailor might well go lee scuppers under.

Lows, Highs and Fronts

A breakdown of weather adages reveals that they are based on a half-dozen or so meteorological premises. The important fact that weather features advance eastward over the earth's surface accounts for a goodly number of the proverbs. By weather features we mean

Fig. 42. "If the Clouds be Bright,
'Twill Clear Tonight."

lows and *highs* and *fronts.* Of these, the low pressure area is dominant. It has been known for centuries that low atmospheric pressure and ill weather go hand in hand:

> Glass high, heave short and away;
> Glass low, let your anchor stay.

And

> When the glass falls low,
> Prepare for a blow;
> When it rises high,
> Let all your sails fly.

It is well to understand the structure of these *lows,* nature's transient weather factories, in order to interpret the rhymes that apply to them. Around the central zone of low pressure revolve the winds (counterclockwise in the Northern Hemisphere). The more marked the pressure difference between the low center and its surrounding air, the stronger is this air flow. As the winds blow around and into the center, they transport air typical of the regions from whence they came—south wind, warm and moist; northwest wind, cold and dry.

Fig. 43. "If the Clouds Look As If Scratched By a Hen, Stand By to Reef Your Topsails Then."

When the wind's in the south,
The rain's in its mouth.

or,

The wind in the west
Suits everyone best.

Not to leave out any important segment of the azimuth,

The wind from the northeast,
Is good for neither man nor beast.

Seafarers of the Atlantic will concede that a nor'easter is not good for man, beast, nor seamen. Fishing is notoriously bad, the wind blows hard and long, and it is damp and penetrating. Air flowing from the northeast means that the low pressure area is to the southwest of the observer and advancing on him. Hence, rain.

The Halo

It is the mixing of different air masses around storms that stirs up trouble. The warm air, forced upward by the cold, denser mass, spreads into sheetlike clouds that are carried ahead of the storm by westerly winds aloft—the same winds that steer the storm in an easterly direction. These clouds are in thin layers far ahead of the *low*, but thicken and lower as the center approaches. The sun or moon shining through them causes a ring of refracted light, a halo. Longfellow described the sequence in his *Wreck of The Hesperus*:

> For I fear a hurricane.
> Last night the moon had a golden ring,
> And tonight no moon we see.

The size of the halo, as seen from the ground, indicates the height of the cloud deck, so,

> The bigger the ring, the nearer the wet.

The halo, as an omen, has been a source of fascination to mariners for about as long as has been the garbage-eating albatross. Here are two more that tell the old story of the golden ring:

> Circle around the moon,
> All hands go aloft full soon.

And

> If the moon shows a silver disk,
> Then putting to sea will be no risk;
> But if she rises with a haloed band,
> Then it is best to stay close in to land.

Most weather maxims with "lastability" have universal application, but there are some that work only for certain locations. High clouds (cirro and alto types) are above the grasp of local weather idiosyncrasies, but often adages are based on low-level phenomena that behave as they do because of terrain or the proximity of affecting bodies of water. Some proverbs that are definitely off-course have persisted down through the years. To stay on the halo theme:

> Never a circle to the moon,
> Should send your topsails down;
> But when it is around the sun,
> With all masts it must be done.

The fact is, a halo is a halo whether it glows from moonlight or sunshine.

Upper Cloud Layer

There is another proverb that foretells a storm if the clouds "go against the wind." This refers to the upper cloud layer and its movement "against" the surface winds blowing into the storm. The distance of these clouds ahead of the storm is almost directly proportional to the size and occasionally the severity of the approaching *low*.

Long foretold, long past;
Short warning, soon past.

If the advance cloud sheet becomes low and thick enough for rain to fall far ahead of the storm's wind circulation, the parent *low* could well be a real topsail-buster.

With the rain before the wind,
Your topsail halyards you must mind;
With the wind before the rain,
Your topsails you can hoist again.

Birds and Fish

Out of the coast dweller's bottomless bag of proverbs can be pulled a handful based on the odd behavior of bird and fish that cannot be explained meteorologically, but, on the other hand, neither can they be laughed away. Who can say that the porpoise and the stormy petrel, in their own inscrutable fashion, have no knowledge of the law of storms? Even the sea gull, not the smartest bird around, may have the key. Folks on the New England coast seem to think so, although it is not quite clear, in the following saying, whether that feathered friend is given credit for forecasting, or being cursed as a harbinger of ill weather.

Sea gull, sea gull, sitting in the sand,
Always foul weather when you're on land.

The Nor'wester and the Nor'easter

But even if we fail to understand why birds come ashore, or why sharks and porpoises play close to the beach when heavy weather is brewing and head seaward at the approach of a cold wave, we can explain the several "long storm" and "short storm" adages, such as,

A nor'wester brings a short storm,
A nor'easter brings a long storm.

Again, the large low pressure area is the "long storm" culprit, and northeast winds in advance are part of the circulation pattern. The squalls that rush down and outward from cumulo-nimbus clouds are local in nature and seldom last more than an hour. Why the nor'wester with this type? In order to qualify as a "storm," a squall cloud must poke its nose high into the air—25 to 50 thousand feet. Cumulus clouds with lower tops are harmless. Therefore, the bulk of the cloud is up in the region of strong westerly winds and the cloud will move with this air current. The strong downrush of wind within the squall cloud exerts itself mainly in the direction the cloud is advancing, which is normally from the west or northwest.

Speaking of breezes,

A veering wind brings fair skies,
A backing wind to be despised.

Take that one with a dash of brine, though. Whether the wind veers or backs depends on the location of the *low*. If it moves to the south, the wind will back, and vice versa. It is true that conditions are worse on the top side of *lows*, but the above rhyme is a bit exaggerated. So is this one:

Winds at night are always bright,
But winds in the morning,
Sailors take warning.

There is some validity there, especially on the open sea. Unlike land areas, wind blows at night over the ocean because of atmospheric instability set up by the warm water (water temperature does not change from day to night) and cooler air. When morning comes, these winds lay at a time when water and air temperature are the same. So, if the wind keeps up through this slack period, there must be a reason; namely, a *low* in the vicinity.

Pleasurable High Pressure

A glance at the weather map will show that the complex, weather-breeding low pressure areas are followed by *highs*, the pleasant domes of air (all of one type air and, therefore, not fraught with mixing trouble) that drift slowly across the surface, bringing cooler weather and light breezes. So,

No weather is ill,
If the wind be still.

As the area of high pressure passes over, the air is clear, and the sun, able to work full time, warms the air and the land below.

If the barometer and thermometer rise together,
It's a very sure sign of fine weather.

The Green Flash

So long as the air in the *high* is crystal clear, it can be assumed that moisture and condensation particles are lacking and rain is not yet near. One excellent indication of a dry atmosphere is to sight the "green flash," or "green ray," and

Glimpse you ere the green ray,
Count the morrow a fine day.

The green flash, startlingly sudden and brilliant, is seen as the upper limb of the sun crosses the horizon. It is the result of the sun's rays being separated into the colors of the spectrum, but blue and violet cannot penetrate the turbid surface air, so red, orange, yellow, and, finally, a flash of green is seen.

A High Followed By a Low

The *high* continues its drift and the winds flowing gently clockwise around it veer from northwest to northeast and, finally . . .

When the sun sets clear as a bell,
There'll be an easterly wind, as sure as hell!

Another old sailor's adage that recognizes the sequence of the passing *high*, followed again by a *low*, states that

When the southeast trades run free and fast,
Then shorten sail for Hatteras.
If safely ye get by Cape May,
Ye'll catch it, sure, in Boston Bay.

In this case, the southeast trades sweeping over the blue Atlantic to the east of the Bahamas result from the circulation around the bottom of the Bermuda *high*. They would normally flow into a developing low pressure area off Hatteras. Maybe the sequence is a bit out of kilter and the sailor gets as far up the coast as Cape May. But his luck is bound to run out in Boston Bay!

But all good things must come to an end . . .

A dappled sky like a painted woman,
Soon changes its face.

And,

When women to the docks do roam,
The morrow they will stay at home.

Because

No one surely pays his debt,
As wet to dry, and dry to wet.

In short, it will rain tomorrow. Other methods for foreseeing the end of good weather are based on the increasing moisture content of the air.

> If the sun goes pale to bed,
> 'Twill rain tomorrow, it is said.

Even though clouds are not yet present, moist air makes the moon look pale.

> Pale moon doth rain,
> Red moon doth blow;
> White moon doth neither rain nor snow.

Fig. 44. "Evening Red . . . and Morning Grey, You're Sure to Have a Fishing Day."

High-flying dust gives the sun or moon a reddish cast and that means that strong winds are howling to the west, tossing aloft some loose real estate, and will soon invade the observer's territory. A white moon indicates an atmosphere clear on any omen-bearing matter.

Stars As Indicators

On moonless nights, the stars will do as indicators of upper-level goings on.

> When the stars begin to hide,
> Soon the rain will betide.

Stars twinkle not so much because of moisture, but by reason of turbulence in the air way up. This turbulence is due to "wind shear," or strong countercurrents of air, and these, in turn, result when the jet stream darts overhead. Ill weather soon follows.

Sound Transmission

High humidity and stable air makes for better sound transmitting characteristics. Many a coastal fisherman can "hear" rain by loudness of distant bell buoys.

When the sound travels far and wide,
A stormy day will like betide.

Heavy Sea Waves

This, plus the fact that heavy sea waves often herald a storm, prompted Tennyson to say,

And may there be no moaning of the bar,
When I put out to sea.

But, what the heck, let it rain. After all,

The more rain, the more rest,
Fine weather's not always best!

CHAPTER 11

A Word About Warnings

Ideally, the weatherwise boatman not only understands weather and is a pretty good "wet-finger forecaster," but also has his boat equipped with radio gear to receive warnings and other weather information.

You must not let the phrase "equipped with radio gear" scare you. Read on, because even the smallest boat can be adequately equipped by one of the new, pocket-sized transistor radios. There is not a boating area in this country that is out of range of standard radio broadcast stations and almost all of these stations do an excellent job of weather reporting.

WEATHER INFORMATION AVAILABLE

Larger craft carry more sophisticated marine radios and many ships are now capable of getting their own assortment of up-to-the-minute weather charts via radio facsimile recorders. But, regardless of equipment, there is a wealth of weather information zipping around the atmosphere in the form of radio waves, waiting to be used by sailors of all classes.

To know what is available is the trick. Ships use a thick book published by the U. S. Navy Hydrographic Office. This tome, *H.O. 206,* tells all that is needed to know about weather broadcasts all over the world. The small craft sailor can get by with much less. An excellent substitute is the Weather Bureau series, *Coastal Facilities Charts.* These sheets sell for ten cents each from the Superintendent of Documents. There are a dozen or so charts, each covering a section of coastal waters and the Great Lakes. They show a map of the area, with locations of Signal Display Sites, Coast Guard Stations, and the locations and telephone numbers of Weather Bureau offices in the area. Details of radio stations include location (pinpointed for direction finding), frequencies, times of broadcasts, and other practical information.

A nice bit of information on the *Coastal Facilities Charts* is the list of Air Navigation Radio Stations. These stations are operated by the Federal Aviation Agency for use by aviators, but they can serve the boatman well. On frequencies between 200 and 400 kilocycles, their prime purpose is to provide "the beam" for aircraft instrument flying. They also give out with weather reports. Weather is given, in voice, for a number of cities within 300 or so miles of each transmitting point. Voice broadcasts, overriding the tone signal, are made at 15 and 45 minutes after each hour. In the big cities where air traffic is heavy, more frequent weather broadcasts are made. Enough weather data is broadcast to construct simple weather maps. Incidentally, this is a good practice for yachtsmen cruising offshore. It is wise to get in some experience copying these broadcasts, however, because at first they seem downright unintelligible. With apologies to the FAA, the weather is rattled off in a monotone that makes sense only after hours of listening. Talk to local aviation devotees for specifics on aircraft weather broadcasts.

Flag and Light Warnings

At signal display sites, the familiar warning flags are flown by day and light signals at night. These sites are usually manned by volunteers who receive the order to hoist signals from the U. S. Weather Bureau via telephone or telegraph. The display towers are standard steel structures, although some sites may use a different method of hoisting flags and lights. Coast Guard stations and vessels fly warning signals, and lightships hoist day flag signals while on station.

The Weather Bureau cautions that display signals are supplementary to warnings issued for broadcast. So, when a tower warning signal is seen, tune in your radio for the complete details, or place a call to the nearest Weather Bureau office.

Flag and light signals and the warnings they represent are explained here.

Small Craft Warning. One red pennant displayed by day and a red light over a white light at night to indicate winds and seas, or sea conditions alone, considered dangerous to small craft operations are forecast. Winds may range as high as 33 knots. Small craft are small boats, yachts, tugs, and barges with little freeboard, and any other low-powered craft.

Gale Warning. Two red pennants displayed by day and a white light above a red light at night to indicate winds within the range 34 to 47 knots are forecast for the area.

Whole Gale Warning. A single square red flag with a black center displayed during daytime and two red lights at night to indicate winds within the range 48 to 63 knots are forecast for the area.

Hurricane Warning. Two square red flags with black centers displayed by day and a white light between two red lights at night to indicate that winds 64 knots and above are forecast for the area.

Responsibility for issuing warnings rests with Weather Bureau District Offices. Along the U. S. coastline there are ten such offices. Chicago handles warnings for the Great Lakes. Smaller inland lakes and rivers are covered by the nearest Weather Bureau office. Bulletins are sent to the Coast Guard, Navy, press, radio and television stations as well as displaymen, so each warning gets maximum treatment.

Coastal warnings apply to waters adjacent to a land area. If inland waters along the coast—the intracoastal waterway, for example—are to be affected, notation is made. For offshore weather, High Seas Warnings are put out via radio stations NSS Washington, KPH Bolinas, California, KTK San Francisco, and KHK Honolulu. The World Meteorological Organization has allocated responsibility to the United States Weather Bureau for areas of the oceans bordering this country, and a portion of the central Pacific near Hawaii. Other nations forecast for their own oceans.

Wind Warnings

Wind warnings are issued on the basis of sustained winds, and not gusts. The wind traces shown in Figures 24–29 will give an idea of how much higher gusts can go over average wind speed. There is no set lower limit for small craft warnings, because this limit will vary widely, depending on whether the wind is onshore or offshore. The exposure of the water area figures importantly, too. Small craft warnings may be issued for rough seas, even if there is no wind. They may also be put out for local thunderstorms, but for the most part, strong and prolonged gradient winds form the basis for wind warnings. Small craft warnings are never issued as a preliminary to hurricane advisories.

The Weather Bureau encourages its forecasters to use discretion in issuing warnings. In areas where seas are normally rough and winds are fresh, warnings are not hoisted as readily as they would be for the same or less severe conditions at a normally quiet place. Boatmen of New England are at home in sea and weather conditions that would disconcert their peers of the placid Gulf Coast.

Here is a sample small craft warning:

> Hoist small craft warnings noon today Delaware Breakwater to Cape Hatteras including lower Chesapeake Bay. Increasing easterly winds becoming 25 to 30 MPH tonight shifting to southerly early Saturday and diminishing to 15 MPH. Tides will be 3 to 4 feet above normal.

Gale warnings may be the first warning put out with the approach of a tropical storm, or they may be based on active pressure systems. Gale warnings may also be issued when thunderstorms are strong enough and plentiful enough to be a hazard to small craft.

Whole gale warnings are associated with intense winter storms or hurricanes. If, in the judgment of the forecaster, dangerously rough seas exist in combination with winds as low as 60 MPH, then hurricane warnings may be displayed. This is done rarely, and only when whole gale warnings are inadequate to tell the story. In such cases, it is pointed out that the storm is not of tropical origin.

Along the shores of the Great Lakes, wind warnings are issued during the navigation season that extends from April to mid-December. During the winter off-season, only general advisories are given, and then only for the roughest storms.

Speaking of winter, it will be well to add a few words about cold weather warnings. Strong winter winds are reported for inland sections with either gale or whole gale warnings. When a fast-breaking howler is winding up, "provisional warnings" are slapped on the circuits and dispatched to the public. This gives the weatherman a chance to gather his wits until he can clarify the situation. In addition to wind warnings and the familiar frost and freeze advisories, the Weather Bureau guards against these other tantrums of the elements:

Cold Wave. A rapid drop in temperature within a 24-hour period to a degree requiring substantially increased protection by the public. What might be a cold wave to Californians could be just a chilly nuisance to Dakotans.

Blizzard. A heavy snowstorm, driven by winds of 35 knots or more. Temperatures must be below 20° F.

Since we are inland, let us stay long enough to talk about other non-maritime weather advisories that are of interest to boatmen as well as landsmen. Tornadoes, squall lines, and thunderstorms are known as "local storms," because they are of localized, convective origin. The Weather Bureau's Severe Local Storm Center in Kansas City, *SELS*, is the nerve center for these phenomena and has forecast responsibility for the entire country. *SELS* forecasters are on

Fig. 45. Small Craft Warnings Were Hoisted for This Squall Line, Now Seen Retreating Southeastward Off the Atlantic Coast

the alert around the clock and they do a fine job. Their warnings are flashed to Weather Bureau offices, which in turn disseminate them to the public.

The bulk of *SELS* "customers" are in the midwestern tornado belt, but lake and river sailors are concerned, too. Many twisters have smashed into lakes and even coastal sections. Tornado alerts are first put out to cover an area of several thousand square miles. Since no one can say just exactly where a tornado will form, this constitutes a danger area. If a storm is sighted, or picked up on radar, then its location and movement are reported on the air. Here is where a radio can sometimes give the listener the few vital minutes' advance notice he needs to seek cover.

Squall lines can be tracked with precision, and their progress forecast with a high degree of accuracy. Isolated thunderstorms, if severe enough, are handled like tornadoes by *SELS*. Here is an example:

> Severe Weather Warning. U. S. Weather Bureau Boston 3:45 PM Saturday July 15.
>
> Radar shows a severe thunderstorm located eight miles south of Woonsocket, R. I. Heavy rain strong winds and one-inch hail are in this thunderstorm. Damaging winds will accompany the storm as it moves ESE'wd from Woonsocket to the coast. It should reach northern Buzzards Bay at 5:00 PM and central Nantucket Sound at 5:35 PM.

When the threat of a severe local storm has ended, "all clear" reports are issued. "False rumor" statements are often made to squelch reckless tales of rampaging storms. One of the occupational hazards of meteorology is the wild weather rumor. Weathermen know that occasionally the most innocuous wind forecast will evolve into bizarre tidings of the elements unleashed by the time it has passed around a bit.

Thunderstorm Forecasts

To qualify as severe enough to be recognized by *SELS*, a thunderstorm must have surface wind velocities, sustained for one minute, of more than 44 knots, or gusts to 66 knots. It must also blaze with frequent lightning. If hail larger than three-fourths of an inch in diameter is falling, it is classed as severe, regardless of wind force.

Forecasts of thunderstorms contain certain descriptive terms that should be explained:

Few. Thunderstorms over an area, or in a squall line, cover up to 15 percent of the area.

Scattered. Coverage from 16 percent to 45 percent.

Numerous. More than 45 percent of the forecast area covered by thunderstorms.

Warning Services

Weather radar stations form an interlocking network now and the number of sites is increasing, particularly along the coasts and throughout the tornado belts, so the boatowner can expect an even better warning service as time passes.

High Seas Warnings, mentioned earlier, are intended for merchant shipping and other blue-water traffic. Broadcasts of marine bulletins are made four times daily for the Atlantic Ocean and twice daily for the Pacific. Special bulletins are sent on receipt. When no storm is about, the bulletin gives that information. Warnings specify either a storm of tropical origin, or one that is extra-tropical. For the latter, there are two categories—Gale, with winds of 34 to 47 knots, and Storm, having winds higher than 47 knots.

Marine bulletins about tropical storms use terminology based on wind force. A Tropical Depression is a closed-circulation *low* with winds of 33 knots or less. When the winds pick up to above 33 knots, but are below 64 knots, the cyclone is called a Tropical Storm. Above 64 knots, it is a full-fledged Hurricane, or Typhoon, if west of longitude 180 degrees. This same breakdown is used in all hurricane warnings.

The Weather Bureau's hurricane warning service is well organized. The central office and research center is in Miami, but other offices have cognizance over coastal and sea areas not covered by Miami. Most Atlantic hurricanes first come under San Juan's responsibility, but soon work their way into that area belonging to Miami. New Orleans has most of the Gulf of Mexico, and Washington and Boston take over when the storm moves to the north of Cape Hatteras.

Advisories

When a tropical cyclone is first detected, an advisory is issued by the office responsible for the area. Subsequent advisories, numbered chronologically, are put out every six hours, at 5:00 AM and PM, and 11:00 AM and PM, Eastern Standard Time. As the hurricane approaches the coast, bulletins are issued as often as every hour. Advisories and bulletins are continued for as long as the storm threatens life and property. After it has passed to the north of latitude 50 N, and to the east of longitude 35 W, the storm's progress is reported only by international marine bulletins.

Advisories should not be confused with warnings. The hoisting, changing, and lowering of warnings is made part of the advisory. When a hurricane may endanger an area within 36 hours, a "hurricane watch" is announced. This is not a warning. Actual warnings are hoisted for winds of gale force or higher.

The format for advisories is standard, and every sailor and coastal resident should be familiar with it. One of hurricane *Donna's* advisories is quoted:

> Miami Weather Bureau Hurricane Advisory Number 24 Donna 11 AM EST Thursday September 8 1960.
>
> Hoist hurricane warnings in the Florida Keys from Key Largo to Key West including Dry Tortugas. Dangerous hurricane Donna now moving towards the Florida Straits expected to cause gale winds after midnight tonight and hurricane winds by late Friday morning. Safety precautions in the display area should be started now and persons living in low lying sections should be ready for evacuation if later conditions warrant. Seas will become very rough and tides abnormally high Friday.
>
> Gale warnings will likely be ordered north of Key Largo later today.
>
> Hurricane watch remains in effect from Melbourne southward to Key Largo and is extended on the southwest Florida coast northward to Fort Myers.
>
> All interests in the central and southwestern Bahamas should continue all precautions for gale to hurricane force winds very rough seas and high tides that will range from 4 to 7 feet above normal possibly higher in a few local areas.
>
> All interests along the north coast of Cuba from Cayo Romano westward should take immediate precautions for hurricane force winds heavy rains and abnormally high tides which will flood all low lands Cape Romano Cuba westward to Archipelago De Sabana tonight and farther westward along the Cuban coast Friday.
>
> Aircraft and island reports indicate that at 11 AM EST . . . 1600Z . . . severe hurricane Donna was centered near Latitude 22.2 North Longitude 76.0 West or about 20 miles west of Ragged Island or about 355 statute miles southeast of Miami. The hurricane continues on a westerly course at near 11 MPH and is expected to move between west and westnorthwest at about the same forward speed during the next 12 to 24 hours.
>
> Highest winds are estimated 150 MPH and hurricane force winds extend outward about 135 miles to the northeast and 90 miles in the southwest semicircle. Gales extend 250 miles to the northeast and 140 miles to the southwest. No important change in size or intensity is expected.

Small craft throughout the Bahamas and along the north coast of Cuba and in the Florida Keys should remain in safe harbor and small craft along the remainder of the south and central Florida coasts should not venture far from port. Shipping in the hurricane path should exercise extreme caution. Heavy rains are expected to continue in the path of the hurricane. It is emphasized that this is a very severe hurricane and all precautions should be continued.

The next advisory will be issued by the Miami Weather Bureau at 5 PM EST with an intermediate bulletin at 2 PM.

Sugg Miami Weather Bureau

Glossary

Air mass: A large batch of air with the same weather properties, such as temperature, humidity, and stability, throughout.

Air mass analysis: A system for analyzing and forecasting weather based on the movement of masses of air. It was devised in Norway during World War I.

Alto-cumulus: A fleecy middle-cloud formation made up of globules larger than those that comprise cirro-cumulus. Sometimes called Mackerel Sky.

Alto-stratus: A middle-cloud type, greyish or bluish in color and usually covering the whole sky.

Anticyclone: A high pressure area.

Apparent wind: The wind as observed on a boat under way. Apparent wind is always different from true wind, either in direction, or velocity, or both.

Arctic air mass: A mass of air that originated in the Arctic regions.

Arctic Sea Smoke: A fog formation consisting of small vertical streamers of condensed vapor. It results when very cold air overlies warmer water.

Atmospheric envelope: The body of air that envelopes the earth. The atmosphere is thicker at the equator than it is at the poles.

Atmospheric stability: A condition of the atmosphere with respect to temperature distribution in the vertical. Warm air over cold is a stable condition, whereas cold air over warm is unstable.

Backing: A counterclockwise change in wind direction.

Barograph: A recording aneroid barometer.

Barometer: An instrument for measuring atmospheric pressure. May be mechanical (aneroid) or mercurial.

Beaufort Scale: A scale of wind force, based on behavior of the sea and such land objects as trees under varying degrees of wind speed. Originated by Admiral Sir Francis Beaufort, of the British Navy.

Bermuda *high:* The semi-permanent anticyclone situated in the middle of the North Atlantic Ocean from late spring until early fall. This *high* is caused by downward flowing air from convergence in the general circulation.

Breaker: A sea wave that has broken into foam. Surf is composed of breakers.

cAk: Continental Arctic air, colder than the ground over which it travels.

Cat's paws: Fleeting patches of rippled water produced by gusts of wind.

CAVU: Ceiling and visibility unlimited.

Cirro-cumulus: Cirriform layer clouds made up of small white globules. Mackerel sky.

Cirro-stratus: A thin, whitish veil of ice clouds above 20,000 feet.

Cirrus: Delicate, fibrous ice clouds, white and silky in appearance.

Cloud billows: Lines of clouds with vertical development, arranged in wavelike formations, usually associated with stratiform cloud layers.

Col: The neutral zone on a weather map that is boxed in between two diagonally-placed *highs,* and two *lows.*

Cold front: The boundary line between cold and warm air. In order to qualify as a cold front, the cold air must be invading warmer territory.

Condensation nuclei: Small particles of chemicals, dust, or salt that attract water vapor droplets. As more and more of these droplets join together, they build into raindrops. Atmospheric ice crystals are especially effective as condensation nuclei.

Condensation trails: Artificial cirrus clouds produced by the rapid cooling of hot and moist jet aircraft exhaust gases.

Convection: Vertical air currents, usually considered in meteorology to imply updrafts.

Convergence: The "coming together" of winds in a horizontal plane. The resulting "packing" causes air to flow vertically upward and downward in a convergence zone.

Coriolis force: An apparent force caused by the rotation of the earth. Winds that would normally blow in a straight line are deflected to the right in the Northern Hemisphere, and to the left in the Southern Hemisphere.

cPk: Continental Polar air mass, colder than the ground over which it travels.

Cumulo-nimbus: The thunderstorm cloud caused by strong vertical currents.

Cumulus: Clouds of vertical development resulting from convective currents.

Cyclone: Any low pressure area, regardless of size or intensity.

Dew: Water drops deposited by condensation of water vapor. Dew forms only on calm nights.

Dew point: The temperature to which air must be cooled to cause saturation.

Doldrums: Belt of calms or light winds in the equatorial region.

Dust Devils: Small dust whirlwinds usually occurring on hot days.

Easterly Wave: A trough of low pressure that moves with the trade flow.

Equatorial Front: The Intertropic Convergence Zone.

Extra-tropical cyclone: A low pressure area, or cyclone, not of tropical origin.

Eye of a Hurricane: Central core of a tropical cyclone.

Fog: Minute water droplets suspended in the air that reduce surface visibility. Fog is classed as follows: Heavy, visibility less than 5/16 of a mile; Moderate, visibility 5/16 to 1/2 mile; Light, visibility 5/8 to 6 miles.

Fetch: A length of open sea over which winds blowing from a constant direction can build sea waves.

Fronts: Boundary lines between air masses of different density.

General Circulation: The large-scale air flow around the earth caused by unequal heating by the sun.

Gradient wind: A weather map wind induced by air moving from a high to a low pressure area.

Halo: A luminous ring around the sun or moon caused by refracted light through ice crystals in cirro-stratus clouds.

High, or high pressure area: A large mass of air that is heavier than the surrounding air. A *high* is normally circular or oval shaped, and its cross section is shaped like a dome. Air flows outward from and clockwise around (in the Northern Hemisphere) a high pressure area.

Historical Sequence: The technique of weather forecasting based on the past movement of features on a weather map.

Humidity: The amount of moisture in the air.

Humidity, absolute: The amount of water vapor in a given volume of air, usually expressed in grams per cubic meter.

Humidity, relative: The amount of water vapor in the air expressed in percentage. Saturation is 100%.

Humidity, specific: A measure of humidity, expressed in grams of water vapor per kilogram of air.

Hurricane: A tropical cyclone with winds of 65 knots or higher.

Intertropic Convergence Zone: A broad band near the equator where the trade winds of the Northern and Southern Hemispheres meet.

Inversion: A condition of stability in the atmosphere wherein a warm layer of air exists over colder air.

Isobars: Lines on a weather map connecting points of equal pressure.

Jet stream: A narrow band of strong winds in the upper air. To be classed as a jet stream these winds must be stronger than 50 knots and should be above 30,000 feet. The velocity in a typical winter jet stream is about 100 knots. Maximum winds are more than 200 knots.

Katabatic: A wind that flows downhill because the air is cold and dense.

Lapse rate: The amount of change of temperature with altitude.

Latent heat of condensation: Heat emitted when water vapor is condensed into visible form.

Line squall: A term, considered outdated, used to describe cold fronts and squall lines.

Low pressure area: A cyclone. An area in which barometric pressure is lower than in the surrounding air.

Mackerel sky: Cirro-cumulus or alto-cumulus clouds.

mAk: Maritime Arctic air colder than the surface.

Mares' tails: Cirrus clouds with tufted ends.

Micrometeorology: The study of small-scale weather effects.

Millibar: A unit used to measure barometric pressure.

Mixing ratio: A measure of humidity, expressed by weight of water vapor present as compared to the amount of water vapor the air could hold at saturation.

mPk: Maritime Polar air mass colder than the surface.

mPw: Maritime Polar air mass warmer than the surface.

mTk: Maritime Tropical air mass cooler than the ground over which it is traveling.

mTw: Maritime Tropical air mass warmer than the ground over which it is traveling.

Nimbo-stratus: A sheetlike cloud from which rain is falling.

Norther: A cold winter wind along the northern Gulf coast caused by a cold air mass moving into the region.

Occlusion, or occluded front: The end result of a cold front overtaking a warm front.

Polar front: The line of demarcation, that extends around the earth, between Polar air to the north and warmer air to the south.

Polar *highs:* Anticyclones formed when air of the general circulation cools and descends near the poles.

Pressure trough: An elongated area of low pressure. A trough differs from a cyclone in that there are no closed isobars with it.

Prevailing westerlies: The prevailing west winds of the temperate zones.

Pseudo-adiabatic: The process that moist air undergoes when it is lifted and cooled due to expansion.

Psychrometer, sling: A pair of mercurial thermometers mounted together, the bulb of one being covered by muslin. This cloth is dampened and, when ventilated, loses its heat through evaporation. The degree of evaporation depends on the amount of water vapor in the air, and so a determination of humidity can be made by comparing temperatures of the dry and wet bulbs.

Radiational cooling: Cooling of the earth, and the layer of air in immediate contact with it, by loss of heat during the night.

Radiosonde: A small radio transmitter that is sent aloft on balloons. Pressure, temperature, and humidity are relayed back to the ground.

Refraction of waves: The change in direction of movement and size of sea waves on meeting a land body.

Roll cloud: The ugly, black cigarlike cloud at the leading edge of some thunderstorms.

Santa Ana wind: A strong, dry wind that blows down through mountain passes near Santa Ana, California.

Saturation, of air: The state of the atmosphere in which the air is holding all the moisture it can. This means 100% humidity.

Sea breeze: A small-scale wind circulation set off by differences in water and land temperatures along the coast. The sea breeze always blows from the sea. Its counterpart is the land breeze.

Sea haze: Moisture and minute salt particles in the air that reduce visibility at sea.

Secondary circulation: Surface wind circulation around *lows* and *highs*.

Secondary cold front: A cold front following a more active "primary" cold front.

Seismic sea waves: Waves of extreme length and speed of movement set off by undersea earthquakes.

Shear-edge: A level in the atmosphere at which two countercurrents are in conflict horizontally.

Squall: A brief, violent windstorm, usually, but not necessarily, with rain or snow. Practically all squalls come from cumulonimbus clouds.

Squall cloud: A large cumulus or cumulonimbus cloud that contains strong downdraft winds.

Squall line: A line of thunderstorms, or other heavy weather, running parallel to, and ahead of, an accelerating cold front.

Stability: A state of tranquility in the atmosphere, induced by a temperature inversion.

Standard Deviation: The amount of "shiftiness" in wind direction. For example, a steady southwest wind may be blowing from a mean direction of 230°, and the standard deviation in direction might be only 10° on either side. On the other hand, a shifty northwest wind might have a mean direction of 320°, and the standard deviation may amount to as much as 45° on either side.

Steering level: The level in the upper air at which winds are most likely to affect the direction of movement of a surface *low* or *high*.

Storm Card: A drawing of the barometric pressure and wind fields of a tropical storm, used in ship maneuvering.

Storm Surge: A mass of water that moves into an area as a result of low pressure and strong winds of a hurricane. Storm surge may arrive as a sudden "tide" or, in its most violent form, as a large wave. Sometimes called Storm Wave and Storm Tide.

Strato-cumulus: A low cloud layer, with some vertical development caused by "rolling" wind currents over the ground.

Stratus: A low sheetlike cloud form. Sometimes called "high fog."

Subsidence: A large-scale settling of an air mass.

Surf: Zone of breakers along a shore.

Swells, sea: Long, low sea waves that do not break. Swells result from the flattening out of wind waves.

Tehuantipecer: A strong wind that funnels down on the Pacific Coast of Nicaragua from a strong high pressure area over the Gulf of Mexico.

Temperate zones: Those areas of the earth between the Tropic of Cancer and the Arctic Circle, and the Tropic of Capricorn and the Antarctic Circle.

Tidal waves: Sea waves of extreme length set off by undersea earthquakes.

Tornado: A small, violent cyclone found over land, and caused by extreme instability in the air mass.

Trade winds: Constant winds of tropical and sub-tropical latitudes produced by the outward flow of air from semi-permanent high pressure areas. The word "trade" was originally allied to the words "track" and "tread," meaning "constantly in the same direction." Later, the term "trade," implying commerce, came into use.

Tropical depression: A closed-circulation low pressure area, of tropical origin, with winds of 33 knots or less.

Tropical storm: Tropical cyclone with winds above 33 knots but below 65 knots.

True wind: The actual wind blowing over a surface. A boat laying to will experience true wind, but once under way, the actual wind will be combined with the forward motion to produce apparent wind.

Turbulence: The degree of bumpiness in the air produced by vertical currents.

Typhoon: A tropical cyclone, with winds of 65 knots or more, in the North Pacific Ocean.

Vapor pressure: The pressure exerted by water vapor in the air. This is another way of measuring humidity.

Veering: A clockwise change in wind direction.

Virga: Rain or snow streamers from clouds. This precipitation is evaporating before it reaches the ground.

Warm front: Boundary line, on the surface, of a mass of advancing warm air.

Warm sector: That portion of a low pressure area composed of warm air.

Waterspout: Small whirling storms over water. They are similar to, but less severe than, tornadoes.

Water vapor: Invisible water droplets always present in the air.

Wet bulb temperature: The temperature to which the air can be cooled by evaporation. This is obtained by ventilating a thermometer whose bulb is covered with a wet cloth. The wet cloth is cooled by the release of latent heat of vaporization.

Windshift line: A surface pressure trough along which a marked change in wind direction occurs. This is normally a front.

Index